HENRY FORD, ENGINEER

ILLUSTRATED BY JOSHUA TOLFORD

HENRY FORD, ENGINEER

By Louise Albright Neyhart

Houghton Mifflin Company · Boston
THE RIVERSIDE PRESS · CAMBRIDGE

The Riverside Press

CAMBRIDGE, MASSACHUSETTS

PRINTED IN THE U. S. A.

TO CARL

WHO SHARES MY INTEREST IN
HENRY FORD'S CONTRIBUTION
TO THE HAPPINESS AND WELL-
BEING OF PEOPLE EVERYWHERE

INTRODUCTION

THIS IS A STORY of a boy who liked machines better than anything. Through his love for machinery he was able to be of great service when he became a man.

Henry Ford was born when America was without household conveniences or mechanical devices. Most of the people lived in the country or small villages. Like the early settlers, families were hard workers and depended largely upon themselves for their needs. Women made clothing from calico and linsey-woolsey, a mixture of linen and wool which they carded and spun. They picked geese and made feather beds and pillows. Rag carpets were woven on hand looms.

Homes were often furnished with plain furniture made in the woodshed. Cooking was done in pots over an open fireplace. A newfangled lamp with a ground-glass globe and a wick soaking in oil was taking the place of

the tallow candle for household lighting. Farm work was accomplished by strong backs, sturdy muscles, and the power supplied by sweating horses.

William Ford, Henry's father, had been born in Ireland. He had come to America in 1847, at the age of twenty, with his brother Henry, and finally settled at Dearborn, Michigan, on the twisting river Rouge. There he worked as a hired farm hand until he had saved enough money to buy forty acres of his own. This accomplished, he married Mary Litigot, the attractive adopted daughter of his former employer, and built a four-room, two-story, frame house on his new farm. The eaves were so low in the front that the rooms upstairs had windows only on the sides. Someday he wanted to add a dining-room and a room for "best."

Mary Ford, who had Dutch and Scandinavian parents, was an energetic girl with a great sense of order. Her hands were never idle, for there were endless household tasks for a Dutch woman who prided herself upon her good food and spotless surroundings. She churned quantities of butter, pressed huge cheeses, made clothes for her family, and found time to help others. Neighbors turned to Mary Ford when they needed a friend for she was kind and good to everyone.

It was this William and Mary who looked proudly at their first child on July 30, 1863. "He is a fine boy, William, let's name him after your brother Henry," Mary said as, beaming with happiness, she held the red, wrinkled baby close. So the baby was named Henry Ford.

That was an important month in American history,

for in it General Robert E. Lee's army was defeated at Gettysburg, and the next day the Confederate garrison surrendered at Vicksburg. At the close of the War Between the States the reunited nation entered upon a period of rapid development. Farming had been the principal occupation, but great changes were about to take place. Trade and manufacturing pushed to the front, and giant industries brought about our great industrial era.

When Henry Ford was two years old, Abraham Lincoln was assassinated. Abraham Lincoln had never seen a typewriter; he had never used a telephone; he had never read by electric light. He had never walked on a cement sidewalk, nor seen a cement road. He had never listened to a phonograph, nor had he seen an automobile.

Yet, during Lincoln's lifetime, especially in the East, roots were sprouting for the gigantic industrial development of America. Mighty forces were being set in motion for the Power Age. We officially entered the Power Age with the steam engine of James Watt, when we learned to attach our tools or machines such as our hand looms, sawmills, potters' wheels, boats, and wheeled wagons to a moving crankshaft. Steam, coal, iron, electricity, and oil were the great factors that contributed to the Power Age.

The steel industry was also taking its first steps. Men were inventing a process for making steel quickly, in great quantities, and reducing the cost. Then the oil industry was born — a short stretch of pipe line was laid in western Pennsylvania, in the valley of the Allegheny River. In 1869 two high-wheeled, large-stacked locomotives huffed and puffed, and panted their way to meet each other in Utah. There were iron rails across America, and passengers and mail could be carried across the country.

During this beginning of a great industrial nation, the small boy, Henry Ford, spent his spare time tinkering, trying to satisfy a natural curiosity about the mechanics of working in metal. He was sure there were more things to be learned in those days than could be learned from his schoolbooks — reading, writing, and arithmetic. The boy's hunger for knowledge instinctively reached out toward the Machine Age.

❀❀ PART ONE ❀❀
1863-1879

Part 1
1863-1879

CHAPTER I

MARY FORD's spotless kitchen gleamed in the fire-
light of the open hearth. The supper was cooking
in pots at the end of a long crane, and the good smell of a
delicious stew was everywhere. There was the rumble of
the churn as Mrs. Ford made butter. Margaret, the oldest
daughter, hummed as she simultaneously mended the
family stockings and rocked baby William's cradle with
her foot. John and Jane were making a game of rolling
a ball of hemp back and forth across the floor.

Henry studied his fifth grade lesson in his McGuffey
reader, and read: "Gambling is the prolific stem, the
fruitful parent, of all vices." His eyes drifted from the
book to the teakettle purring on the crane. He wished
Mr. McGuffey's book would tell about things a ten-year-
old boy would like: discoveries — pieces that would fit
together to make something useful, a story about a black-

1

smith shop, or big, high-wheeled, chugging trains.

The steam continued to pour from the spout. Henry watched it intently, and forgot about his lesson. He knew that steam was the power that turned wheels, but he didn't know why. Like James Watt, who had discovered the principles of the steam engine a hundred years before, Henry liked to take off the lid of the teakettle, and put it on. Then he would hold a cup over the steam, watching the vapor swirl from the spout and condense into drops of hot water.

"Mr. Steam, Mr. Steam," Henry mumbled, "why do you always run away? What would you do if you were a prisoner and couldn't get out?"

But Mr. Steam went right on singing his merry tune. Henry turned to his mother, "Ma, what if the teakettle didn't have a spout, and there couldn't be any big cloud of steam?"

"Now, how would I know then whether the water was boiling for the tea, and what would I do for baby William when he gets the croup?"

"But just supposin', Ma," Henry persisted.

"You stop bothering your head about that and settle down to your lessons. We don't want folks to say the Fords' oldest child is a dumkuff!"

The door opened and Mr. Ford came in from the barn. "Humm," he sniffed, "Irish stew. "I'll match my wife's cooking with any woman's in this county."

Mrs. Ford smiled gratefully. She was always pleased when her husband praised her cooking.

Jane and John ran to their father and clung to his legs. "I'm going to take off Pa's boots tonight," John said.

"No, let me, Pa. Let me!" Jane insisted. "And will

you tell us another story about the leprechauns?" she begged.

"More stories about Ireland and those little Irish scamps?"

Mr. Ford sat down in his big chair and stretched out his feet. "Here's a boot for each of you. We'll have a story after supper."

Henry moved closer to his father. "Pa, if the steam couldn't get out of the kettle, what would happen?"

"What does it say in your book?"

"The book doesn't tell about steam."

"Then why do you think about such things when you should be reading your lesson? You learn what is in your book. After you learn all that's there and you still want to learn more, we will figure out how many bushels of oats we will get from an acre next year."

Henry put his head back into the book and waited impatiently for supper.

The next afternoon Henry was alone in the kitchen. The tick-tock of the clock on the shelf grew louder and louder. Henry's heart thumped as each tick-tock seemed to shout, "Find out, find out."

He climbed to the top of the cupboard shelves and

found an old clay teapot. He poured a dipper of water into it, tied the lid on with a piece of wire, and plugged the spout securely with one of baby William's bootees.

"Now, just try to get out!" Henry challenged, as he hung the teapot with its many bindings over the fire.

Henry sat down on the floor to wait.

Finally, there was a tiny gurgling sound; then a great rumbling; and then — BANG, BANG! BANG! Bits of the teapot were everywhere. A piece broke a window, another broke the fruit dish on the table, and another gashed Henry's head.

Henry's mother heard the crash and hurried in from the garden. "Henry, you're scalded and bleeding. What happened?"

"I found out what would happen if the steam couldn't get out of the teakettle," Henry said with deep satisfaction.

"I should have known you'd find out. This might have been a serious accident. You better get this windowpane fixed before your father notices it — he'll have no patience with your curiosity," Mrs. Ford warned.

Henry's thoughts were not about his father at that moment. "Ma, Mr. Steam is a lot stronger than I suspected," he said with great awe.

"See that you remember how strong he is," Mrs. Ford replied as she dressed the wounds.

While Henry and his mother were picking up pieces of broken glass and china, Margaret ran into the house, calling excitedly, "Pa just drove into the yard with a surprise for you, Ma. He won't tell what it is. Hurry up, Henry, Pa wants you to help carry it in." She stopped abruptly when she noticed Henry's bandaged head.

"Henry, you've been hurt!" she exclaimed.

Mrs. Ford thought it best to treat this accident as lightly as possible and not discuss it. "Just a little cut," she said firmly. "We'll say no more about it. Come, let's see what your father brought," she added gaily.

John and Jane were already gathered about their father trying to investigate the big, mysterious wooden box.

"What can it possibly be?" Mrs. Ford asked thoughtfully.

"You couldn't guess in a hundred years," Mr. Ford said with a twinkle in his eye. "One of the seven wonders of the world — come lend a hand, Henry."

"One of the seven wonders of the world," Margaret, Henry, Jane, and John repeated.

Just then Mr. Ford got a glimpse of Henry's head. "What you been —— "

"Now, William," Mrs. Ford interrupted, "it's nothing. Just the teapot. Henry's all right. Nothing serious at all. This present surely has me guessing," she added, bringing the smile back to her husband's face.

Henry breathed a sigh of relief. His mother was an angel. She had a nice gentle way of soothing his father when he became irritated. Now his father had his mind back on the box, and the teapot incident would be dismissed without further explanation.

Henry tugged at the box. "Gee, it's heavier than lead, Ma."

"See that you don't drop your end, lad," Mr. Ford cautioned. "This cost me a pretty penny."

Carefully the box was placed on the kitchen floor, and board by board it was uncrated.

Everyone watched intently as bits of black painted

iron and shiny varnished wood were exposed. A large wheel appeared.

"I haven't the faintest idea what it can be," Mrs. Ford confessed. "Henry, you figure it out. You're smart about such things."

Henry already was busy figuring out the mystery. "It's a machine, Ma, a sewing machine," he said breathlessly.

Mr. Ford told about his great present. Instead of turning the wheel by hand, this machine had the new improved treadle to drive the wheel. Now Mrs. Ford would not need to spend long hours in needlework to make the family clothes.

"But it will take an expert to make it work," Mrs. Ford said, in dismay.

Mr. Ford scratched his head. "By George, it looked so simple when Abe Reecer showed me how it worked. It sews in a short time what it would take hours to do by hand. But I'll be jiggered if I can remember what he did."

"Pa, you just let me examine it," Henry said eagerly. He located the needle and the bobbin, which was a slender pin to hold the thread. He took a spool of white thread, secured the spool in the bobbin, and wound the thread through some shiny knobs and loops on the machine. He found a piece of cloth. He gave the wheel on his right side a spin. His feet rocked on the iron treadle. The needle across from the wheel started jumping up and down.

"Stitches!" Mrs. Ford exclaimed. "It's a miracle!"

"Stitches!" Margaret, Jane, and John echoed, wide-eyed with wonder.

"Didn't I tell you it was a humdinger?" Mr. Ford beamed triumphantly.

Henry's stitches zigzagged across the cloth. Mrs. Ford tried it next.

"I'll need some practice — I'm half afraid of it now," Mrs. Ford apologized for her imperfect stitches. "It will save hours of hand-sewing. Margaret, you are old enough to use the new machine, and Henry will keep it in good repair. He will know just where to oil it. But no one else must touch it," she said with authority, carefully placing the shiny wooden cover over the top.

After the box-cover was on the sewing machine, Henry kept thinking about the wheel and the pulley over which the belt passed. Things went through his head that would not occur to the average boy his age. If he knew the farthest distance through the wheel and the farthest distance through the pulley, he could figure how many revolutions of the pulley would be produced by one revolution of the drive wheel. Then, by carefully turning the pulley one complete revolution, he could find how many stitches the machine took in each complete revolution, which would be the amount of useful work accomplished.

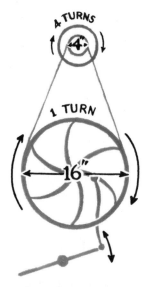

CHAPTER 2

HENRY NUDGED his seat-mate, Edsel Ruddiman, and whispered, "Tell the gang to meet after school. I've got a big idea for a lot of fun." Edsel waited until the teacher's back was turned. Then he passed the word to Will Bennett, John Haggerty, Rennie Field, and John Ruddiman.

There were two schools near the Ford farm, one was two and a half miles one way, and the other was two and a half miles the other. Henry started at the Scotch Settlement School but after a few years changed to the Springwell School, taught by Mr. Brush.

The school building was a one-room affair, painted white, with double wooden desks and benches, and a badboy seat in the corner.

The very moment Henry was developing his brilliant idea for a lot of fun, Mr. Brush stood before the class tracing Columbus's voyage to America on a map. He stopped suddenly. "Henry, stop that constant jingling. Must I tell you each day to leave the contents of your pockets on my desk, or keep that junk at home? I'm losing my patience."

Henry walked to Mr. Brush's desk and emptied his pockets of everything but his pocketknife. Out tumbled bolts, nuts, nails, washers and other odds and ends of machinery — Henry's usual treasures. He went back to his seat and tried to keep his eyes on the map, but they kept straying towards the hands of the clock, and with his knife he carved his initials in his desk.

After school the boys met under the big oak tree, down the road.

"Well, what you got up your sleeve, Henry?" Rennie asked.

"It's down at Roulo Creek."

"Bet it's just a dead frog or somethin'," Will Bennett said.

"Yeh, let's play mumblety peg," John Ruddiman suggested.

"You know, Henry always thinks of things none of the rest of us ever think of — like making something that moves. You better stick with us if you don't want to miss the fun," Edsel warned.

So they all started for the little creek that emptied into the River Rouge.

Henry told the boys to build a strong dam. "This is going to be a real honest-to-goodness dam that'll furnish power to turn a wheel that will run a mill."

From under the bushes Henry hauled a rake handle, a discarded coffee-grinder, and a wooden wheel that he had made. The boys watched with great interest.

"See this old coffee-grinder?" Henry said, "that's going to be our mill. She'll run from the water power from the dam."

"You mean the coffee-grinder will work without us turning the handle?" Edsel asked in amazement.

"Sure thing," Henry said with the greatest confidence in his project. "I got it all figured out. Edsel, you and Rennie and Will get all the big stones you can find, and you other two fellows get the sand and the mud ready."

While the boys were building a strong, watertight stone dam across the creek, securing it with turf and piling up mud and sand, Henry was rigging the wheel, the rake handle, and the coffee-grinder together and installing it.

The water rose rapidly. The boys watched the contrivance intently. The rake handle, acting as a shaft, ran from the wooden wheel in the dam to the coffee-grinder. Before the grinder would work, the wheel would have to turn. The wheel didn't budge. The boys looked at each other questioningly. Maybe Henry didn't know what he was doing. Henry didn't say a word. He was studying and retracing each step in his plan. He couldn't understand why the wheel wasn't turning.

Then, as if by magic, it started to move a bit. Twelve eyes were glued to the wheel. Rippling water broke the stillness. It moved a little more, slowly and jerkily; then it made a complete revolution. Faster and faster the wheel turned, until it was actually spinning smoothly.

Henry filled the coffee-grinder with hunks of hard turf and loose, fine dirt came tumbling out. Each boy took his turn putting chunks of earth into the mill. Even

John Ruddiman admitted this was more fun than playing mumblety peg.

Already Henry was thinking about perfecting and enlarging his mill. "You know," he said, "I think I could rig up a bigger mill, and a bigger wheel that would grind anything. It would really be useful and do work."

"How long would it take to make it?" Will asked eagerly.

"I might be able to work on it tonight. It all depends on the chores Pa has laid out for me."

The boys left the creek with great plans for their new power plant.

All would have been fine if only John Miller, an indignant neighbor, had not come to school the next day, protesting in rage. He thumped his fist on Mr. Brush's desk. "Those boys of yours have dammed up Roulo Creek and the water has flooded my cellar where my potatoes are stored!" he thundered.

Mr. Brush knew exactly where to put his finger on the ringleader. "How about this, Henry?"

Neither Henry's honest confession nor his accomplishment impressed Mr. Miller. To soothe the injured farmer, Mr. Brush spoke spiritedly on the rights of others and told the boys to tear out the dam.

"But Mr. Brush," Henry pleaded, "that water wheel really worked and we were going to see if there was enough water power to run a larger mill. Water power can save a lot of work that we have to do with our muscles. We could channel the water so it wouldn't overflow."

Mr. Miller shook his finger at Henry. "That boy will come to no good," he shouted angrily. "His head is full of mischief!"

The irate farmer was influential with the school directors, and Mr. Brush could not satisfy him and be sympathetic with Henry at the same time. Looking very uncomfortable, Mr. Brush said, "There shall be no more dam building."

Henry's chin dropped. "I'll bet I won't let any old Mr. Miller run me when I'm a man," he told himself, defiantly. His plans were smashed. He was sorry about Mr. Miller's cellar, but he did think he should be given a chance to try to control the water. He was disappointed in Mr. Brush, too. Surely Mr. Brush knew that moving water has force, and we should learn to use force to move things.

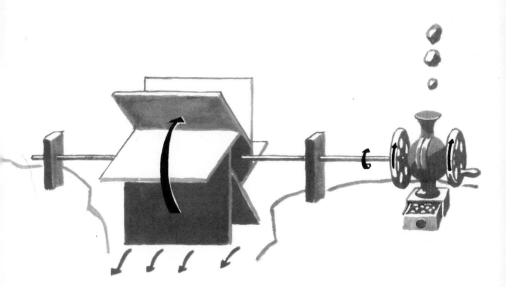

CHAPTER 3

S PRING WAS AS challenging in Dearborn as in any other farming community. It meant a great deal of hard work for the farmer. The land must be made ready for the growing season. It had to be plowed, put in shape, and then planted. By this time Mr. Ford had added a great deal more land to his original forty acres. There were two regular hired hands, but even so, the help of Henry and John, the two oldest boys, was badly needed.

After the seeds came up, the crops had to be cultivated and the weeds kept out. Henry thought this was a back-breaking business. He disliked the barn chores even more. He bargained with John to do the milking, while he took over the care of the horses. Horses, he thought, were a heap more intelligent than cows. Cows were stupid and smelly. In the summer the flies bit and the cows swished you with their tails when they were milked.

Henry liked haying best of all. The men used to swing big scythes but now his father had a new mowing machine, drawn by horses, to cut the sweet-smelling grass. There was always the fragrant spiciness that seeped into Henry's nostrils, and he enjoyed it as he would a tasty morsel.

When a nest of quail was uncovered in the cutting, Henry would move the birds to a safe home. He liked birds and watched for their return in the spring. He knew the song of each one: the wild canary, oriole, blue-bird, thrush, wren, and many more. There was friendly cheer in their sweeping flight and song. They were valu-able friends, too, for they ate the insects that were enemies to the crops.

Henry's father was a natural born farmer, with a great love for the land, and a strong desire to make the most of its possibilities. Although he was not mechanically minded, Mr. Ford thought that farm machinery saved a man time, effort, and money. He was one of the first to own a mowing machine and a reaper in his community. Henry was very excited about the new machines, and in no time at all he knew them from A to Z. Not only did Henry study his father's machines, but any other he could find in the community.

Two years had passed since the teapot had exploded and Henry wanted to know more about how the energy of steam was put to work and how it was controlled. A short distance from the Ford farm was an old deserted sawmill that stirred Henry's interest every time he passed it. One afternoon Henry stuck a few tools under his arm and started for the old mill to find out how steam was regulated to enable saws to do the work of men.

The machinery lay on the ground in the sawdust. Someone had taken the head off the cylinder of the engine and left it that way.

Henry rolled up his sleeve and stuck his arm in to locate the steam ports and find out how the slide valve controlled the steam.

As he groped for an opening or a lever, the sawdust suddenly gave way. The heavy cylinder rolled over on top of him. He was caught in a trap. He could not remove his arm unless he could turn the cylinder over, and this he did not have the strength to do without help. He lay very still, trying to determine the best plan to release himself.

The cylinder could not be lifted, but it could be rolled down a slope. With his left hand he reached around and started to dig away the sawdust on the other side to make a trench into which the cylinder could roll. He dug and dug. It was a slow and tiresome procedure, but finally the cylinder rolled over and freed his arm. He tested it gingerly. Fortunately, it was not broken or even wrenched.

Immediately he went back to his exploration. He found the slide valve in the steam chest, and discovered that it moved by the valve gear. It opened and closed a passageway by sliding over a port, alternately admitting

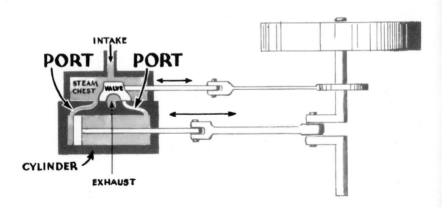

INTAKE

PORT PORT

STEAM CHEST VALVE

CYLINDER

EXHAUST

steam to the piston and releasing it. This moving part
gave Henry an idea.

He hurried home to his workshop, where he hoarded
his tools. He had a forge and bellows, which he patterned
after the one in the Dearborn blacksmith shop; an anvil,
on which he could hammer hot metal into any shape he
desired; a vice and a bowstring-driven lathe. His collection of junk was immense — scraps of metal, broken bits
of farm machinery, bolts and nuts, and pieces of wood.
In this little shed Henry repaired broken tools and farm
machinery. To make something useful or repair something to make it work again was his chief delight.

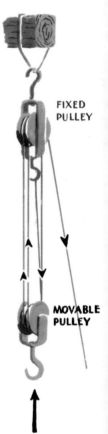

FIXED
PULLEY

MOVABLE
PULLEY

That morning he had worked on a gadget to open and
close the barnyard gate without getting out of the carriage. He had experimented with a fixed pulley and it
just wouldn't work. The slide valve gave Henry the idea
that perhaps the contraption needed a movable pulley.
A fixed pulley would change the direction of a force, but
a movable pulley could be used to increase the force, and
the more movable pulleys that are used, the easier it is
to move the weight.

Henry brought boards from the workshop and installed
one perpendicularly to the gate. Horizontal boards were
attached to the top of the perpendicular one, and extended from each side of the gate, at buggy-seat level.
The pulley and ropes connected the gate latch with the
horizontal boards. One only needed to pull the rope
which dangled from the horizontal board and the gate
opened.

Just as Henry was testing his new contraption, his
father appeared, driving a team of horses hitched to a
wagon. "Open the gate, Henry," he called.

"Drive up to the gate, Pa, pull the rope, and see what happens," Henry instructed.

"Now, what tomfoolery have you been up to?" Mr. Ford asked impatiently. At the same time, he pulled the rope curiously. Strangely enough the gate opened and Mr. Ford smiled. "Seems that for once you made something practical."

"Go through the gate, Pa. Then pull the rope on the other side and the gate will close."

Puzzled, Mr. Ford shook his head. "If you're so smart about such things, I can't for the life of me see why you aren't more interested in what's in your schoolbooks. Well, jump in the wagon and you can go to town with me."

Henry lost no time in getting into the wagon. A trip to town meant a visit to the blacksmith shop. He could smell the hot metal when he just thought about it. The blacksmith in his leather apron would let Henry operate the great bellows that blew up the fire in the forge to a white heat. It was exciting to hold a piece of red-hot metal in the fire, then work it into a new shape on the anvil.

Suddenly, as Henry and his father rounded a curve in the road, they came face to face with a huge, black, iron vehicle moving along by its own power. Sooty clouds of smoke shot from the stack. It seemed like an iron monster laboriously bumping and rumbling down the road on huge rollers. The rear wheels turned by a chain something like a bicycle.

"Pa, stop!" Henry shouted, standing up in the wagon. "It's what I've always wanted to see, a steam engine without horses to pull it!" Henry jumped out of the wagon and darted across the road.

"Say, Mister," Henry yelled above the noisy engine, "can I see your machine?"

The man stopped.

"What makes it move? How does it work? What can it do?" All in one breath Henry eagerly asked questions.

"Hold on, young feller," the driver laughed, "one at a time."

"What are you going to do with it?" Henry asked, as he walked around the great giant, absorbing each detail.

"We brang this here machine to Dearborn for drivin' threshing machines, runnin' sawmills and such," the man said, and went on showing Henry how he stood on the platform behind the boiler to shovel coal and do the steering while the machine joggled along the road by its own power.

He explained to Henry how the chain that made the engine move could be taken off and a belt put in its place for driving other machinery. He showed him how the chain could be shifted so the wagon stopped but the engine kept on running.

"Come along, Henry," his father called, "we got to be getting along."

"Just a minute, Pa, please!" Henry begged. "The man didn't show me how the steam is generated."

"That beats all — didn't think a lad would care a hoot how it was generated. You're bright as a dollar, by gum. Most boys just like to see the wheels go 'round. Well, we got two parts, the engine proper and the boiler. Now, in this here engine proper you got a cylinder. In there

a piston moves up and down from the steam in the boiler. That steam comes over to the cylinder through this here steampipe. See this little thing? That's a throttle valve. I turn that to adjust the amount of steam entering the cylinder.

"I want to see the ports and slide valve work," Henry insisted.

"Well, if that don't take the cake — a kid knowin' 'bout ports and slide valves. You're too smart for your breeches. Here they be, right near the ends of the cylinder."

"How fast can the engine go?" Henry asked.

" 'Bout 200 revolutions a minute. I govern it by that there throttle. I'll be switched if you ain't got more questions in you than bees in a beehive! Bet you'd like to run one of these some day, eh?" the driver asked.

But Henry didn't take time to answer; his father had already started down the road, and he had to run to catch up with him.

"Henry, you have no idea of time," Mr. Ford said impatiently, as Henry climbed into the wagon. "Look where the sun is!"

"Won't I have time to go to the blacksmith shop?"

"Not today, we'll be late for supper."

That night Henry tried to build a model of the road engine, but it was several years before he built one that ran very well. He had learned that steam has force because water takes up more space when it changes to steam. He had studied and repaired the windmill on the farm and learned that moving air has force. When he built the dam, he learned that moving water has force. These great forces, Henry reasoned, could move things and do many things that muscles could not do.

CHAPTER 4

IT WAS SUNDAY MORNING and the family was enjoying a good breakfast of buckwheat cakes and maple syrup. A new stove with an oven had replaced the fireplace method of cooking, and Mrs. Ford could cook the golden brown cakes as fast as the family could eat them. Margaret, who was now thirteen, and a tall young lady, carried them to the table and passed them to her father, Henry, John, Jane, and the two hired men. William sat in his high-chair spooning his oatmeal all over his face, and a new baby, Robert, was in the cradle.

Henry's thoughts were dismal. This was the day he must be polished like a pewter candlestick, and go to church service.

When the chores were done, Henry set about encasing his feet in stockings and stiff shoes, and his neck in a white stiff collar. He could neither wiggle his toes nor turn his head.

"Everybody ready?" Mrs. Ford called briskly, as she took a quick peek at herself in the mahogany framed mirror, seeing that her dark hair was smooth under her bonnet, and that her white collar on her blue linsey-woolsey dress was spotless.

Mr. and Mrs. Ford rode in the front of the new surrey with the fringe around the top. Henry, John, Margaret, and Jane climbed in the back seat. "Doc," one of the hired men, would keep an eye on William and the baby while the family attended service.

"Why do we have to go to church every Sunday?" Henry asked vehemently.

"Shame on you, Henry!" Mrs. Ford spoke sharply. "A noisy sermon is good for the soul."

When they reached the church, and Henry was tieing the horses to the hitching post, the Bennetts drove up.

"Hey, Henry," Will called, "I've got something to show you."

Henry and Will walked to one side as the morning worshippers greeted each other outside the church.

"It's my very own, my grandfather gave it to me." Will proudly held up his shining watch. Watches in those days were not the small, delicate ones of today, but big, almost clocklike affairs that were wound with a key.

"Gee wilikers, let me hold it," Henry exclaimed, looking longingly at the watch, "I promise to give it back."

Will gingerly handed Henry the watch.

"But it isn't running," Henry discovered, after holding it to his ear and trying to wind it.

"Well, it's a watch anyway — even if it doesn't run. It's better than none," Will bragged.

This was a great opportunity for Henry. He had been

itching to examine the inside of a watch for a long time. "You know, Will, I might be able to find out what's wrong and make this watch run for you," Henry suggested eagerly.

"Naw," Will said cautiously, "it's all right this way."

"But if you could actually tell time with it — think how important you'd be to all of us fellows."

Being important appealed to Will, and he remembered how Henry had made the wheel run at the creek, and how he had fixed farm machinery.

All thought of church was gone and the boys dashed away to the farmshop in Bennett's barn.

First, Henry took off his collar and his tight shoes. Of course there were no tools in the shop fine enough for the delicate work. But by filing a small nail to the right size and shape, Henry made a tiny screw driver. Will sat at Henry's side, never once taking his eyes off his precious watch.

Henry carefully laid the small pieces on a table. What he saw made him think of his mother's wringer — one wheel was used to turn another by means of teeth or cogs that intermesh. In the wringer the work was done when the handle was turned. In the watch the power to drive the wheels was derived from the mainspring, and the balance wheel was used to obtain uniform speed. The force from the mainspring would keep the balance wheel from stopping. This was an exciting discovery to Henry.

Mrs. Ford, in the meantime, had discovered the absence of her son, and when he did not appear at the close of the service, she decided her worries were justified.

The Bennetts and the Fords searched everywhere for the boys. When they were finally discovered in the shed,

Mr. Ford's anxiety turned to anger. No punishment, though, could erase the thrill of this experience for Henry.

"It runs. I fixed it!" Henry beamed, holding up the watch for inspection. "Just needed a little cleaning. It was as easy to put it together as it was to take it apart," Henry told them triumphantly.

Word soon spread throughout the neighborhood that Henry, who was now fifteen, was a crackerjack at regulating and repairing watches. He developed a great skill as well as a great delight for the fine and delicate work.

His first tools were a nail, tweezers (made from a corset stay), and a pair of knitting needles. Soon he rigged up a lathe in his room and did his watch repairing there. With a kerosene lantern on the floor to give a bit of warmth to his feet, Henry would bend his head close to his work, nudge the balance wheel, and life and motion would come back to the timepiece. Fixing a watch was fun and not work to Henry. Each watch he repaired was a new and thrilling experience.

Watches hung from a board in his room, waiting their turn to be repaired. The owners were particularly enthusiastic about Henry's work because he did not charge for his labor.

It was a good thing for Henry that he had this keen interest in watches to occupy his attention, for these were sad days in the Ford household. Mrs. Ford had died. There had been a great understanding between Henry and his mother, and he missed the sympathetic attitude she had for his tinkering. Now that she was gone, the house was like a watch without a mainspring.

Mrs. Flaherty, a cousin of the Fords, came to live with them and take care of the children. This arrangement went on until Margaret was old enough to assume the responsibilities.

Henry was glad to go to his room at night, for he did not like to sit in the family circle without his mother there. The pleasant evenings with his mother playing the organ and the family gathered about her, singing hymns, were now a haunting memory.

The watchwork was always waiting after his school and farm work was done. Sometimes he would saddle a horse and ride many miles to do a repair job.

One night it stormed while he was gone. The streams were running high, and a small bridge washed away during the evening. On the return trip, not being able to see that the bridge was out, Henry and his father's best horse plunged into the stream. For a few tense moments they floundered in the darkness. Fortunately, neither suffered more than a good drenching.

Mr. Ford was waiting for Henry at the barn door. When he learned what had happened he was red with rage. "This is no laughing matter," he boomed. "You not only risk your own life, but you take my best sorrel.

What if she had broken a leg — we would have had to shoot her!"

"The sorrel's all right. She didn't get hurt."

"Lucky for you," Mr. Ford said sternly. "Now look here, Henry, your labor is worthy of hire. I forbid you to do any more free work. You're a growing boy, and you need your rest. And furthermore, you are to leave the horses in the barn."

Henry couldn't understand his father's reasoning. If he did his farm work well, he couldn't see why he shouldn't be allowed to spend his leisure as he wished, doing something he liked.

He went to his room to do some thinking. As long as his father believed all of his ideas were a lot of foolishness, there would always be a clashing of wills. He knew he could never bend to his father's wishes and follow in his footsteps on the farm. With a great love for engines and machinery surging inside of him, he would never be happy filling his days with an endless round of chores and farm work. He could see only one course open to him. Tomorrow he would start his own way of life.

PART TWO
1879-1896

PART 2
1879 - 1896

CHAPTER 5

IT WAS STILL dark when Henry jumped out of bed and made a bundle of a few pieces of clothing. There was not a stir in the house. Henry moved about quietly. He listened for the rhythmical snoring as he passed his father's door. Carefully he avoided the steps that creaked as he came down the stairs.

Grabbing a large hunk of coffeecake from the pantry, Henry was out of the house and on his way. The first streaks of dawn were just breaking through the horizon. The sky was dotted with blackbirds, circling and chattering in the large willow near the house.

The tall spindling boy tingled with his freedom. For years he had known that what he wanted to do most in life was to learn everything there was to learn about engines. He thought of his mother patting his shoulder and saying, "Henry, you're a born mechanic." The smattering of mechanical knowledge he had picked up on the farm had sharpened his appetite.

Surely a boy sixteen, he thought, should have no trouble keeping himself in a big city like Detroit, if he were willing to work hard. And he was willing to work very hard. He must satisfy this impelling urge to make things, to take materials and turn them into something that moved, or into tools that helped to make other things. Only a city could give him more knowledge about these things.

Henry walked briskly. The scarlet woodbine, the trees and shrubs, tinted with their first fall shades of gold and crimson, were wet with morning dew.

All the way to Detroit Henry's thoughts were mingled with the adventure of new machines and the pleasant memories of good times on the River Rouge. Deep down inside, Henry wished his father could understand that the country was not the same as he found it years ago when he was a lad from Ireland. The business of making things was getting to be as important as farming. Surely a good mechanic would be as useful to his country as a good farmer. More and more people were going to cities to live. He remembered his teacher saying that in 1810 Detroit's population was only 1,650. Now, in 1879, there were over 110,000 people living in Detroit.

Smokestacks and church steeples loomed in the distance. The nine mile walk had seemed like only a short jaunt — there was so much to think about. Henry wiped the perspiration from his face, for the sun still held some of its summer warmth. Then he dusted his clothes with his handkerchief and shined his shoes as well as he could. He was ready for his new life.

The waterfront of the Detroit River was a busy place. Henry wished he had time to watch. Carloads of grain, lumber, meat, fish, flour, and hides were being loaded on steamers and schooners. Dirty little children were climbing and running about, calling to each other in different languages.

Detroit looked like a giant blacksmith shop to Henry. There were factories making carriages, stoves, hoop skirts, organs, and candles. The main streets were paved with cedar blocks, and the side streets were mud or dust depending on the weather. There were wooden walks raised from the streets to protect the pedestrian from the carriages drawn by spirited horses.

The streets were filled with fancy hacks, horse-drawn cars with bells that jangled furiously, bicycles, and teams of horses pulling wagons. There were four-story buildings that seemed almost to reach the sky.

A sign over one of the smaller buildings read: James Flower & Company, General Machinists. Henry had heard this was one of the better shops; one which did machine work and made steam engines as well. He knew this was a shop where he could get a good start in mechanics.

He opened the door confidently. That the shop might

not want nor need a young, inexperienced boy did not occur to him. He only thought about how anxious he was to learn and how well he would do his work. Inside there was noise, grease, cranes, flapping belts, and dismembered engines — everything he wanted to get into.

In one corner of the room a man was working at a desk. Henry waited until the man looked up and then said deliberately, "I came to work."

"What can you do?" the man asked.

"I came to learn all there is to know about working with machinery."

"What have you done?" was the next question.

"I've repaired farm machinery, and I know how to handle tools. I've fixed watches, and learned about the operation of a steam engine."

"And you want to work?"

"I not only want to," said Henry, "I like to work."

Concluding that the boy had grit and determination, and above all confidence in his own ability, the man said, "Be here at seven o'clock tomorrow morning. Your wages will be $2.50 a week."

Everything seemed right with the world as Henry left the shop. He wished he could start his job at once, tomorrow seemed so far away.

The next thing was to locate a place to live. Henry thought he might find some advertisements in a newspaper. Down the street he could hear a newsboy screeching, "Free Press, Free Press, read all about President Hayes's speech." Henry bought a paper and read that the President wanted a great many reforms to improve conditions.

Turning the pages of the paper Henry found a few

lodging houses listed on the last page. Up and down the streets Henry trudged from one house to another, trying to find one where he could have room and board for $2.50 a week. But the rooms were dingy and dirty and did not measure up to the standard of cleanliness his mother had taught him.

There was only one thing to do and that was to pay more for clean living accommodations and find a second job to increase his income. He had less than $5 in his pocket when he left home. Three-fifty of this he paid for a clean room. He would have to earn another $1 a week for his living expenses.

He remembered seeing a watch repair shop in the business district, and he lost no time going back there. The owner offered Henry $2 a week if he would come at seven o'clock each night and work until eleven. The lure of the princely wage of $2 for four hours' work on watches while he worked eleven hours to earn $2.50 at the machine shop did not bother Henry in the least. He wanted to know and master each fascinating step in the life of a machine.

Meanwhile, when Henry did not appear for supper Margaret was in a frenzy. Some terrible accident had happened to her brother, she was sure. The hired men and Mr. Ford hitched up and drove separate ways to look for Henry.

They discovered the young man had not been in school. Someone had seen him walking towards Detroit. On hearing this Mr. Ford said, "The boy can take care of himself. There is nothing to worry about. He'll be back as soon as he learns the foolishness of his ways."

After two days with no word from Henry, Mr. Ford could stand it no longer. He drove his sorrel to Detroit to look for his son. The search was not difficult for it was only sensible to inquire in the machine shops. When he located Henry at the Flower Company, he asked the foreman if the boy might come outside to talk to him.

"Henry, you belong in school," Mr. Ford said, sternly.

"Pa, I can't go back to school. What's the good of the old school — reading, writing, and arithmetic — I want to learn about engines. Gee, I don't know how to tell you, but it's like the hungriest feeling a fellow ever had."

"Pshaw, Henry, this engine business is a silly fad. In a few years people will forget all about engines. Now farming you can always depend on. There will always be farming."

"Times are changing, Pa," Henry argued. "More and more things are being made by machines, and are made better."

"Don't you believe such truck, Henry. How could a machine make better harness than old Si Henricks has been making for forty years. And take Jed Martin, there isn't a machine that could make as fine a pair of shoes as he can. They might use those machines for awhile but not for long, 'cause they'll break down. Machines aren't dependable."

Henry shook his head and laughed. "People have to learn how to repair those machines and build better ones."

Mr. Ford jingled the coins in his pockets as he wondered just what action to take with his stubborn son. What he felt like doing was boxing his ears and yanking him home, but he knew that was no solution for the determined Henry. If he forced him to come home, he would only run away again. Finally, he said, "Well, get this machine craziness out of your head and then come back to the farm." He shook hands with Henry and drove back home.

CHAPTER 6

E ARLY EACH MORNING Henry reported at the shop.
Everything interested him; the men arriving, the
starting up of the machinery, the knowledge which the
employees seemed to have about their work.

He was happy as a lark with his new life. His daily
routine fitted into twenty-four hours like the pieces of
a jigsaw puzzle. He was up at six in the morning, from
seven in the morning until six at night in the machine
shop, from seven to eleven in the evening at work on
watches with an eye loupe, which is an eyeglass that mag-
nifies. Then he rushed to his room to read technical
journals that he bought with his extra money, and finally
to bed for a few hours' sleep. The long hours never tired
him, and each morning he got up brimming with vigor
for the new day.

Henry regarded a machine as fondly as a bosom pal.

He hovered over it, cleaned it, polished it, and beamed when it purred smoothly. When he left the shop he felt great satisfaction, not because he had earned a day's pay, but because he had learned a lot and liked his job.

Every new task challenged and fascinated him until he mastered it. On the farm he had thought about the work and wondered how it could be made easier. Now he studied the machine shop the same way.

It wasn't long before Henry could see flaws in the way the shop was managed. Nothing was ever made twice alike. Time and material were wasted. A piston rod had to be made over because it wouldn't fit the cylinder. Parts were cast, recast, and filed down to fit other parts. Henry was switched from one piece of work to another to help complete an order delayed by poor organization. This helter-skelter management was irritating to Henry. But he knew he was there to work and learn and not to change things.

Although Henry's work was so satisfactory that his pay was raised to $3 a week, he became restless when he had learned everything in the shop. He quit his job after nine months and went to work for the Dry Dock Engine Company at fifty cents less a week.

The Dry Dock concern was the largest in Detroit and made only marine engines. It was the kind of engine which was universal from about 1860 to 1890, and which is still used for ships of moderate speed.

The power is applied at one end of a long shaft and given out at the other. The high-pressure cylinder is fitted with a piston valve, because with this form, there is the smallest friction and most perfect balance under high pressure of steam.

Marine engines are always of the compound condensing type for economy of fuel and economy of water. Each
particle of steam that can be trapped and condensed after
leaving the engine must be returned to the boiler. The
air pumps and condensers must be highly efficient, so the
last unit of energy can be extracted from the steam, and
return as much as possible of that steam to the boilers.

There was a lively gang of young fellows in the new
shop, and Henry was immediately accepted as one of
them. They had a lot of good times together. They
played practical jokes on each other, and wrestled and
boxed. They wandered about the broad streets lighted
with naptha lamps, and watched the horsecars whiz past.
Some of the boys visited saloons with swinging doors and
sawdust floors, but Henry didn't go along with them. He
thought they were foolish to spend their money on something that could only be harmful to them.

The boys worked just as hard as Henry, but to them
it was only a way to earn money with which to live and
have fun. After their apprenticeship was served, they
would become full-fledged machinists and draw bigger
pay, marry, and raise families. It did not occur to them
that engines might be improved. They were satisfied with
things as they were.

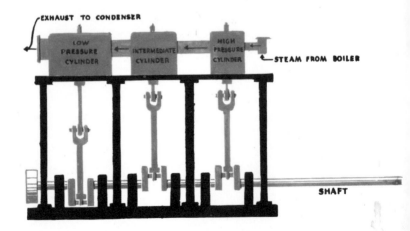

Detroit was an exciting place to live. The Prince of Wales visited the city and stopped at The Russell House. And one day the great General Grant came to attend the reunion of the Army of the Potomac. Three years earlier Alexander Bell had given a personal exhibition in the city and now some of the people were communicating with a queer device called the "telephone." There was one central exchange, twenty-two wires, and three hundred semi-private phones.

Henry gave up the night job at the jeweler's shop. His wages had been raised to five dollars a week so it was no longer necessary for him to keep such a rigid routine. Before he left the shop he bought a three dollar watch.

He took the watch to his room and took it apart. Spreading the pieces before him on the table he saw that it consisted of simple parts made from the cheapest metal. He couldn't understand why the watch should cost so much. Either the manufacturer was making too big a profit or he was allowing tremendous waste in the manufacturing, Henry reasoned.

One night when the boys from the Dry Dock Company gathered in Henry's room, he showed them his watch and again spread all the parts on the table.

"Say, what's the idea of ruining a good watch?" one of the boys said. "You'll have to throw that in the ash pile."

"Any old day!" Henry laughed. "It's as easy as rolling off a log to put it back together." Then seriously, he said, "I think we ought to start a watch factory."

"Start a watch factory!" the boys repeated in amazement. "What gave you that idea?"

"The three dollars I paid for this watch," Henry said. "Why, if we made watches by the thousand, all exactly

SCREW

alike, and every part cut by an exact die, eliminating all waste in materials and energy of the workers, that watch could be made for fifty cents. Everybody could own one. Everybody needs a watch."

Henry shoved the cheap little pieces of metal about for the boys to examine.

"What do you mean by eliminating waste energy of the workers?" a red-haired boy asked.

"By having efficient machines to do the work and installing them to save waste motion and steps. Why, over at the plant the men are falling over each other half the time, looking for the right tools," Henry explained.

"Yeh, we sure do," the boys agreed. They had never thought about it before — that there might be a better way to work.

Henry got out a paper and pencil and started to figure. The boys watched with great interest.

"We could build a good watch that would cost thirty-seven cents and sell it for fifty cents. We could produce two thousand watches a day. A daily profit of two hundred and sixty dollars," Henry estimated.

This sounded wonderful to the boys — all except Red, who said, "We'd be saps to sell the watch for fifty cents. Why not ask two dollars for it, and really clean up on the profits?"

Henry's face got red and he replied angrily, "That isn't the kind of business our country needs! I would never be connected with a business that thinks about money before it thinks about service. When I run a business, I will make something the people need. I'll use good materials and produce as economically as I can, produce as much as I can, and sell as cheaply as I can — that's my idea of running a business; then the money will come honestly."

The other boys, seeing the chance for making much more money, sided with Red. Henry argued that lower prices increased sales and that higher prices would keep sales down.

"We're dunderheads to fool around with our jobs," a boy named John said emphatically. "There's a fortune in your idea, Henry, if you see it Red's way."

"Not on your life, fellows," Henry said, staunchly. "It's the service that's important. You can't be greedy about money and have a successful business, at least not one that will last for years."

"You're crazy as a loon, Henry," John retorted. "What do we care about service just as long as our money piles up. Two dollars is a cheap price for a watch."

Henry put the pieces of the watch together, and shook his head in disgust. "I wouldn't sleep nights if I thought the buyer wasn't getting his money's worth, and I wasn't giving him a square deal."

"You're an old fuddy-duddy, if I ever saw one," John said. "Nobody ever made any money in business with scruples like yours!"

Henry smiled. He didn't care what they called him, but they could never change his ideas about running a business. "Laugh if you like," Henry said, "but someday I'm going to have a factory and make things by the thousand because I believe quantity is the answer to manufacturing for the fellow with an average income — then he can afford to buy more."

All the time Henry was talking he was putting the watch back together.

John picked the watch up and listened to it tick. "Henry," he said, "you've got brains. It's a shame you're such a crack-pot!"

After the boys left, Henry thought about his watch factory ideas. He wished he had the money to start it. He was sure he could show manufacturers a few tricks about producing watches in quantities and selling them at cheap prices, and still make money.

JRT

CHAPTER 7

I T WAS LATE one night when Henry went to his room and found a letter on the table. The letter was a long one. He read it and read it again. Then he sat thoughtfully on his bed for a long time.

Henry had made swift progress in learning mechanics. He had finished his apprenticeship as a machinist much earlier than the regular three years. Now he was "road expert" for Westinghouse portable steam engines. This job gave him a practical side for his learning. He installed, repaired, and taught others how to run steam engines. There was nothing Henry liked better than a balky engine — in no time at all he had it purring like a kitten. Each time he repaired an engine he learned something new.

The letter was from his sister Margaret. Things were not going well on the farm, and she begged him to come home. His brother was ill and his father had met with an accident. The hired men just didn't work without a boss.

Henry could understand how badly he was needed on the farm, but the last thing in the world he wanted to do was to leave Detroit. He thought about his mother and her ideas of service to others. If he did go back to the farm, there was one good thing about it: he would have time to experiment with engine building in the workshop.

Back to the farm he went. Seeing Henry in his old environment may have made Henry's father and neighbors wonder if he hadn't had enough of engines and the city. But this never occurred to Henry. He had no idea of settling down on the farm.

Dearborn was beautiful in the spring. The bobolinks and wrens were back, too. The green fields, budding trees, flowers, and birds made up for what he was missing in Detroit.

Henry peered about his old workshop, and smiled. His old tools were little more than a child's tools. He could now replace these with real machines to equal his knowledge and technique.

The lathe, vise, forge, and anvil, that had served him well, were replaced by a better forge, a lathe driven by foot power, a drilling machine, and excellent hand tools. There was now a skilled machinist, twenty years old, in command of the shop, instead of the exceptionally clever boy who had handled tools with instinctive ease.

"If I could make a farm locomotive," Henry thought, "we could do away with the horses that eat their heads off all year in order to work during the planting and harvesting seasons!" No farmer had even told Henry that a team of horses and a plow were not good enough as a power plant for plowing. But it seemed foolish spending so much time on a job if it could be done in a much shorter time and with less effort.

After the day's work was done on the farm, Henry went to his shop to build a farm locomotive that would eat only when it worked. He used the cast-iron wheels of an old mowing machine. He made a pattern and cast a cylinder for the steam engine that was to drive the locomotive. The engine had only one cylinder, the bore was 3 inches and the stroke $3\frac{3}{4}$ inches. Inside the cylinder he fitted a piston which was to be moved up and down by the force of steam generated in an upright boiler. The fuel was wood.

There was great excitement the day of the test. The farm hands, Margaret, and her father were all out in the field to watch. Henry was sure his farm locomotive would plow a whole field in a short time. He built a good fire in the boiler. The water started to boil, and up and down went the piston, chuggety-chug, chuggety-chug. Then the big wheels started to turn very slowly.

Everyone watched intently. It was actually running. The air was tense with excitement. It ran about forty feet and stopped. "Not enough steam was generated quickly to keep the engine doing its work," Henry told his disappointed audience.

"Too bad," Mr. Ford shook his head impatiently. "It's a failure. It only ran forty feet."

"But it ran forty feet, Pa. That's progress!" Henry said with great confidence. He did not admit for a second that his dream was a failure. He felt that he had proven that if the "farm locomotive" could go forty feet,

one could be made that could travel as long as was desired.

It simply meant that he had much more to learn about
building engines. A light machine could not handle a
heavy boiler. He remembered his experience with the
teapot when he was a small boy. There was danger in
using a light boiler for steam. There were drawbacks to
steam. Henry remembered a magazine article he had
read while he was working for the Flower Company. A
workman had brought the paper from England and had
loaned it to him. It told about a German named Otto,
who had invented a four-cycle gas engine. It had a single
piston which moved up and down by gasoline. There was
time for the gas to be compressed in the cylinder head
before the explosion took place. For each explosion the
piston travelled twice up and twice down; a total of four
times for each power impulse. "I wish I could have a
chance to repair an Otto engine," Henry said to himself.
"It sounds good to me.

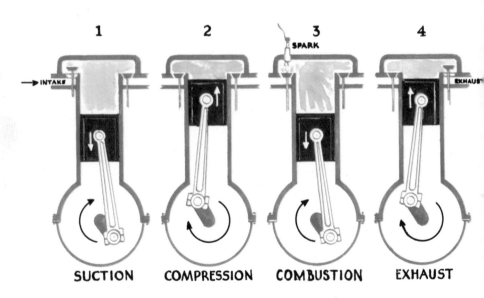

1　　　2　　　3　　　4

SPARK

INTAKE　　　　　　　　　　　　　EXHAUST

SUCTION　　COMPRESSION　　COMBUSTION　　EXHAUST

CHAPTER 8

"HENRY FORD, I'M THOROUGHLY out of patience with you," Margaret scolded, when she came home from church one Sunday morning.

"What have I done now?"

"Ever since you went to church with us the first Sunday you were home, the girls have been so excited about my good-looking brother, who has come back from the city — and you pay no attention to any of them."

"Is that all that's ailing you?" Henry sighed with relief. "Girls — fiddlesticks! They titter and chatter like jenny wrens. I like to listen to birds, but not girls!"

"Some day you'll meet the right one, and then you'll change your mind in a hurry. Boys like you always fall in love with a thud."

"You can have all the beaus you want, but girls don't interest me," Henry declared.

47

Mr. Ford sat in his Hitchcock rocker, listening to the conversation with a twinkle in his eye.

"I'm not through lecturing," Margaret said, standing with her hands on her hips. "You came home when everything was topsy-turvy Pa was worried. But now the cows are giving more milk, the corn is cultivated, the fields are in fine shape, and the farm machinery is back in condition. Even the hired men are working like beavers. There isn't any reason why you shouldn't have a good time with the rest of us young people instead of keeping your nose in that workshop every night."

"Anything else on your mind?" Henry laughed when Margaret stopped to get her breath.

"Yes, I'm going to give a big harvest party in a few weeks and you are to be a pleasant host. Please, Henry, be nice to all the girls!"

Henry was silent and looked at his father in despair.

The day of the party arrived late in October, when the fields were brown with stubble. Hours of work went into the preparation of the great supper. There were baked hams, fried chicken, cottage cheese, baked beans, succotash, home-made bread, chocolate cake, angel cake, lemon pie, raisin pie, cherry pie, blueberry pie, and peach pie.

At the long table Henry's eyes kept falling upon a certain young lady with soft brown hair and kind gentle eyes. Her name was Clara Bryant. She was the daughter of a prosperous farmer about eight miles up the road.

When the others were husking in the big barn, and each young man fought for the red ears of corn that gave permission to kiss the girl of his choice, Henry's eyes still followed Clara. He liked the way she laughed and her quiet manner.

Then the fiddler called: "Sets in order. Swing your partner. Do-se-do. Do-se-do and around we go." Clara had partners waiting for the whole evening.

"Shucks," Henry thought, "maybe I'm missing something by not knowing those square dances." He decided to have Margaret start teaching him tomorrow night. He'd be the best doggoned square dancer in the country.

When the party was over, Henry summoned all his courage and asked Clara if he might call on her Wednesday evening.

"I'm sorry," Clara said, indifferently, "someone else is calling on me."

But Henry wasn't one to give up easily when he set his mind to something. "Miss Bryant, when may I come?" he asked desperately.

Clara laughed softly. She didn't have the heart to refuse this shy persistent young man. "Come next Sunday, if you like," she said.

Henry had six days to think about Clara before he would see her again.

Getting to see and talk to Clara was not easy, even if she did say Henry might call. Often he found other horses tied to the hitching post and their young drivers

visiting with Clara. On these occasions Henry would sit in the kitchen with Clara's mother and father and talk about the late President Garfield and the new man, President Alan Arthur.

Snow came and Henry battled on to win the fair Clara. He made a sleigh, painted it bright red, and groomed his father's sealbrown mare like a show horse. Clara liked the cutter and the jingle of the sleigh bells, and she did find a little more time to see Henry.

There were ice-skating parties and Henry proved himself a master on skates. The young people would start at the Ford farm and go down the River Rouge to its mouth, and then up the Detroit River as far as Belle Isle, near the entrance to Lake St. Clair.

Margaret was very pleased that her brother had joined their good times. "You know, Henry, you're not an old stick-in-the-mud since you met Clara," she said. "I'll bet you wish you were her only beau."

"Sure wish I was," Henry admitted, "but I'll cut those other dudes out before long."

Then one day Henry's rating really went up with Clara. He made a watch with two dials and two sets of hands. A new time was being introduced, a standard railway time, which differed from the regular sun time. Clara was very impressed to see a watch which could tell two kinds of time. Henry told her how he made it.

That night Clara went home and told her parents that she liked Henry. "He's different from all the other young men I've known. He's so sensible and serious minded. Someday he's going to make his mark in this world," she said.

"Having a little snooze?" Henry asked his father one day when he saw him stretched out on the horsehair sofa.

"Just a little cat-nap. Won't need these much longer. I'm just about fit-as-a-fiddle again."

Margaret was cleaning the corner cupboard, carefully washing and polishing the Delft china and the thumb-print glassware.

"I'm not going back to Detroit," Henry announced like a bolt out of the blue.

Margaret almost dropped one of the lovely blue dishes and Mr. Ford sat upright on the couch.

"I knew you'd come to see things my way," Mr. Ford said happily. "The farm beats these city jobs every time."

"It isn't that, Pa, but I guess I'll be getting married."

"Oh, Henry!" Margaret exclaimed excitedly, "Clara will make you a fine wife."

"She appears to be a right nice young lady," Mr. Ford agreed. "I'll give you the south forty. There will be enough lumber from the timber for a house and build-ings."

Henry started sawing lumber that very day. All winter he cut trees and turned them into lumber. He bought a circular sawmill and a 12 horsepower engine to run the saw. Sturdy oaks, maple, and beeches fell to the powerful stroke of his ax. Then the mill turned them into boards. In the spring he hired a man, and together they built a house with wide porches for Clara. Henry wanted the most wonderful girl in the world to have a fine house.

CHAPTER 9

IT'S EVERYTHING I'VE ever wanted," Clara told Henry when they came back from their honeymoon in Detroit and moved into their new house. She happily pointed out the patchwork quilts and the crocheted tidies she had made. These were things a man would never notice but they did add such a stylish touch to the furnishings. She loved the new varnished mission furniture, the flowered brussels carpet, and the beautiful lace curtains. There was a fine new wood-burning range in the kitchen, and even a pump in the sink that Henry had fixed so she would not have to carry water from the well.

Henry ran his own farm even better than he managed his father's. His orderly mind organized the work so it was done smoothly without overworking his hired help, but still saving labor and time.

Clara did a good job of managing too. Her house was

as neat as a pin. Canned fruits, preserves, and vegetables were lined up on the shelves in the cellar. Her pantry was always filled with cookies, cakes, and pies. Everything was going along exceptionally well for young people just starting out. It was a good year for crops and they were realizing a fine profit.

Each night when Clara cleared away the supper dishes, Henry got out his mechanical journals and devoured them word for word. After the dishes were washed, Clara would mend or crochet, rocking comfortably on the other side of the large, kerosene table-lamp.

It was on just such an evening that Henry slapped his magazine on his knee and sat erect. "Clara, they're on the right track," he said.

"What track?" Clara asked patiently.

"A horseless carriage! Some Frenchman has invented a horseless carriage. Clara, suppose I could make a horseless carriage?" Henry said, his clear blue eyes sparkling with enthusiasm.

Clara put down her mending. She knew Henry was very serious. "I'm sure you could, Henry, if you set your mind to it. But why bother about that? We've got everything we need."

"It isn't for us, Clara. It would make a new kind of life for people," Henry explained. "We would have to move to Detroit," he said, and waited anxiously for Clara's reaction.

Move to Detroit! The thought was almost more than she could bear. Give up her nice new home and good profits from the crops in exchange for a meager existence in a city while her husband experimented with an idea that everybody would laugh at! Many other things flashed across Clara's mind. There would be no money for pretty calico prints. There would be no time for Henry to take her skating and to square dances.

Clara knew that this was more than a case of spring fever that a dose of sulphur and molasses could cure. Finally, she said, "Henry, when you make up your mind to do something, there is no turning it aside. You would not have a happy, peaceful moment if you did not follow this urge — I know your restless nature like a book. If that's what you want, we'll go to Detroit. And you'll make your horseless carriage. I believe in you!" she said earnestly.

Henry's eyes told Clara everything she wanted to know. He was happy that he had such an understanding wife. Her confidence was all he needed.

All the rest of the summer Henry planted, plowed, and tended the cattle with his heart and mind on a gasoline engine. By fall he leased his farm to his brother.

"Will we come back to our house after you build the gasoline engine?" Clara asked wistfully, as she looked about the bare house after the furniture was loaded on wagons.

"Sure, we'll come back," Henry said, patting her shoulder reassuringly.

The neighbors all gathered to say good-bye. Clara wondered if Henry realized that they thought he was addle-brained — leaving a good profitable farm for goodness only knew what — at best it could only be a greasy old machine shop. What if he did make one of those thing-a-ma-jigs, that would run? What would he do with it and who would want it, as long as folks had a good horse that was safer and cheaper?

Detroit had grown. It covered nearly thirty square miles along the Detroit River. The population was about twice as large as it had been ten years before when Henry first walked to town to learn about engines. There were many new factories. Electricity was gaining favor. The Edison Electric Company had three sub-stations in the city.

Henry thought he had better learn something about this new source of power. His knowledge of steam engines helped him secure a job at one of the sub-stations. The current was generated in the sub-station by steam, and Henry was just the young man who could fix anything that went wrong with these engines.

The little house the young Fords moved into was on Bagley Avenue. There was an old brick shed in the rear which was just the spot for Henry's machine shop. He bought good machinery for his shop, a small drill press, a large drill press, two metal lathes, a wood turning lathe, a small forge and anvil. He installed an electric motor for his power source. He built racks around the walls to hold his small hand tools. Everything was brightly polished and in perfect order.

Henry was happy to be back in Detroit. Here he was close to engines. He had a shop in his backyard where he could work on a horseless carriage. His job at the Edison Electric Company would give him a chance to find out a way to create a spark. If he were going to build an engine that ignited gasoline some part of it would have to supply a steady spark to explode the gasoline for power.

It was interesting to study the dynamo. The upper part was a big electromagnet, shaped something like a large horseshoe, or like a U upside down. Between the ends of the magnet was a coil of many loops of wire, called an armature. When the armature was turned, each of its loops moved past the magnet, starting electric currents in them. When the electric current passed through the armature to the commutator and brushes, it became a direct current and ready to be used.

In the evenings Henry read about Michael Faraday's experiments. It was a fascinating story of how a young scientist learned that moving a loop of wire past a magnet would create an electric current in the wire. Then Henry studied Thomas Edison's work. Edison knew that his electric bulb would not be very useful until he invented machinery to supply the electric current for bulbs. Many inventors had made dynamos after Faraday's first one, but all the dynamos were wasteful. Over half of their power was turned into heat, which made them too hot and too expensive to work well. So Edison improved his dynamo until it wasted less than a tenth of its power.

The men in charge of the Edison Electric Company soon saw that they had a good man, and Henry was made manager of the mechanical department. In this job of manager he did a lot of thinking about the men working under him. He questioned the wisdom of working twelve-

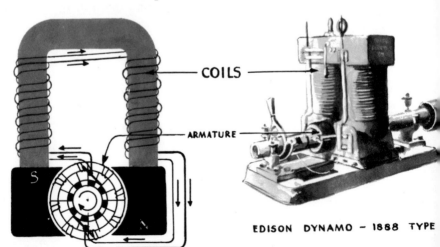

COILS

ARMATURE

EDISON DYNAMO – 1888 TYPE

hour shifts. The employers believed that men, like the rest of their equipment, should be worked to the limit of their strength. There were about forty men on the regular list of workers and five substitutes. The substitutes were kept busy all the time because some of the men were sick or tired every day.

It would be good business to take better care of their men, Henry thought. He believed that paying them well and improving their working conditions was practical common sense, and the sooner people realized that the sooner we would have a world that would be better for everybody.

"Why, if the machines broke down as often as the men, you would be having all kind of fits!" Henry told an executive.

"Ford, you're a good man, but you've got a lot of hoity-toity ideas. They sound all right, but they aren't practical. Why, if we turned you loose, you'd have everything upside down and ruin our organization."

Henry could not convince his superiors that the men would do a better job working shorter hours, so he went on working from six to six in the Edison plant and keeping his management ideas to himself.

After work Henry would hurry home to a hot supper and then to work on a one-cylinder stationary engine mounted on the kitchen sink. The cylinder was a tube from an old boiler. It was on this experiment that he learned to make a gasoline engine fire. Clara stood by his side each evening dropping gasoline from a teaspoon into a lubricator which fed the carburetor. She waited anxiously for the even explosions. Her reward was the smile of satisfaction on Henry's face.

CHAPTER 10

THE CARRIAGE TOOK shape one Sunday afternoon as Clara and Henry sat in the parlor talking about things that were happening: the Johnstown flood, the admission of the States of Washington, Montana, and the Dakotas into the Union, and the inauguration of President Benjamin Harrison. Suddenly Henry grabbed a small piece of paper and drew a sketch. "This paper isn't large enough, Clara," he said. "Is there a larger piece handy?"

Clara picked up a piece of sheet music with a plain back. On the blank side of the music Henry drew plans for his little motor vehicle. It was a vehicle that would generate its own power and carry two passengers.

There were men in America and abroad who were striving for the same end — a horseless carriage, but Henry had no way of finding out what they were doing.

He was alone in his work and had to figure everything out for himself.

During the Civil War a Frenchman, by the name of Lenoir, used a spark plug which fired constantly and created so much heat it was impractical. Then Otto, a German inventor, released his four-cycle-principle gas engine. Henry got to repair one of these engines at the Eagle Iron Works, and was greatly impressed. A downstroke of the piston in the cylinder drew in the gas, an upstroke compressed it, the expansion of the ignited gas forced the piston down, and an upstroke exhausted the waste gas.

Some inventors were working on electricity as the power for a horseless carriage. But there were several difficulties to this development. The batteries that had to be carried along were heavy, and it was necessary to recharge them often.

Every night and far into the morning Henry worked on his little motor vehicle. He worked methodically, always drawing a plan and developing each detail on the plan before starting to build. Making and breaking the spark, cutting down weight in the engine and securing suitable materials were some of his most important problems.

He had to make each part that was needed and it was often difficult to find the necessary material.

The engine was finally finished, but the steering gear, which was the tiller-type, was giving trouble. There had to be a mechanism powerful enough to turn the front wheels against the pull of the engine, yet pliable enough to make a short turn quickly.

"You know, Henry," Clara said one night as she held

the light and passed tools to her husband, "that nosy Mrs. Baxter next door got my temper riled when I was hanging up clothes this morning."

Henry was absorbed in fitting parts together. "What's bothering Mrs. Baxter?" he said indifferently.

"Oh, it's just that the neighbors keep hearing your tools, and the clank, clank of the engine, and see the light in the shed until all hours. Now some of them are saying you're crazy."

Henry laughed. "You didn't let a little thing like that upset you?"

"Henry, how can you joke about such a thing? I told Mrs. Baxter just what I thought of her for even listening to such stories. I do wish you'd get that vehicle finished so we could live like other people." Clara wiped a few stray tears from her eyes.

"There, there," Henry dropped his work and put his arm around her, "you're all worked-up tonight. The vehicle is almost done. This isn't like you at all. After the baby comes you'll be too busy to listen to Mrs. Baxter's stories."

"Let's go back to Dearborn," Clara sobbed.

"Now, now, things aren't that bad," Henry's voice was comforting. "We'll go into the house and I'll make you a cup of hot tea. We'll forget all about the shop."

After they finished the tea and Clara was smiling again, Henry went out to the shed to lock it for the night. A lot of things were flashing across his mind. Clara did have to make a lot of sacrifices so he could work on his horseless carriage. Maybe for Clara's sake they should go back to Dearborn to live. But he had had so many interruptions and the vehicle was almost ready to run. It was puzzling to know just what to do.

He locked the door. Then he opened it again. Perhaps just a few more minutes on that steering mechanism would have her ready for the testing. Instantly every ounce of his energy and all his thoughts were lost in the steering lever.

Several hours passed. There was a light tap on his arm. "Henry, we've got to stay here and finish the horseless carriage. That was just a foolish notion of mine about going back to Dearborn."

But Henry scarcely heard Clara's words. "I've licked it, Clara. It's ready — ready to test!" He was so excited that his voice was only a husky whisper.

"But it's three o'clock in the morning and it's raining hard," Clara reasoned. "Don't you think you better wait until daylight?"

"No matter — I should jump out of my skin if I had to wait that long!" Henry said, as he threw the shed doors open.

The night was very dark and the rain was turning the snow into slush. Henry hung a lantern on the front of the car and mounted the buggy-seat he had installed. At first there was a sput-sput-putt-putt-putt. Clara held her breath, releasing it and breathing freely only after the jumpy sputterings settled down to a regular chug-achug-chug, chug-achug-chug.

Then, as if by some strange magic, the motor car actually moved. Henry tightened his grip on the steering lever and managed to keep away from Mrs. Baxter's fence. The strange looking contraption joggled down the street, zigging and zagging to keep in the wagon tracks.

Clara, wrapped in her woolen shawl, ran along the wooden sidewalk, keeping pace with the car. Lights appeared in upstairs windows and a few of the more curious

and venturesome souls came out to see what was making such a commotion.

At the end of the block Henry jumped out, lifted his contraption around, drove it home, and pushed it back into the shed.

"It works!" he shouted triumphantly. "Now, I've got to improve it and make it practical. It has to be driven through mud, ruts, and up hills. It will have to run backwards, too."

Henry knew there were a lot of faults to his four-wheeled vehicle with bicycle tires. But he *had* built an engine with two cylinders having a two and a half inch bore and a six inch stroke over the rear axle. It could develop four horsepower with two speeds, a high of twenty miles an hour, and a low of ten. The speed was regulated by a clutch lever in front of the driving seat. Three gallons of gasoline could be carried in a tank under the seat. This was fed to the motor by a small pipe and a mixing valve.

The year 1893 was very important to the young Fords. The horseless carriage had run its first test, and then a son, Edsel Bryant Ford, was born. The baby was named after Henry's school chum.

Word went about that a queer man was driving a queer contraption around the streets of Detroit, and it was considered a nuisance. It made a racket and scared horses. But its worst offense was blocking traffic. A crowd always gathered to look at it. If Henry left it alone for any length of time, some curious person would try to run it. Finally he had to carry a chain and chain it to a lamp post whenever he left it anywhere.

Henry spent four years building this puffing little machine, scarcely larger than a bicycle. Then he took two more years to think about his second gasoline car before he started actually to build it.

By this time there were a few high priced cars being manufactured and sold to the wealthy. These cars had large complicated engines, which needed massive bodies. To most people it seemed that young Ford was left trailing in the dust as Winton, Haynes, and Duryea put their cars on the market.

Henry was thirty-three years old in 1896 when one of the great events of his life happened.

"I have good news!" he called as he rushed into the house after work.

Clara was just tucking Edsel in his bed. She tiptoed out of the bedroom and softly closed the door. "What is it?" she whispered eagerly.

"I've been chosen one of the four men from the Detroit company to attend the annual convention of the Association of Edison Illuminating Companies at Manhattan Beach in New York."

"That is a splendid honor," Clara beamed.

"I hope I'll meet Thomas Edison, he's going to be there," Henry said hopefully.

A few days later at Manhattan Beach the forty-nine-year-old Edison stood on the porch of the Oriental Hotel and shook hands with young Henry Ford. At a dinner in the evening the electric carriage was the center of conversation. One of the executives addressed Mr. Edison and pointed to Henry, saying: "There's a young man who has made a gas car."

Mr. Edison was immediately interested and asked how the car worked.

Henry described it.

"Come closer, young man, so I can hear you better," Mr. Edison said.

Henry changed places with the man at the right of Mr. Edison.

Mr. Edison looked at all the men at the table and said, "There's a big future for any lightweight engine that can develop a high horsepower and be self-contained. No one kind of power is ever going to do all the work of the country."

The electrical genius asked Henry one question after another. Henry drew sketches to illustrate his answers. Mr. Edison was particularly interested in the contact arrangement for exploding the gas in the cylinder.

"Young fellow, that's the thing. Keep at it!" Mr. Edison said, bringing his fist down on the table with a bang. "The storage battery is too heavy. Steam cars won't do either because they require a fire. Your car has no fire, no smoke and no steam. You have the right thing. Keep at it!"

Creepy little shivers tingled up and down Henry's spine. That bang on the table from the greatest inventor

in the world was more than an incentive to spur Henry on. No one, other than Clara, had ever given Henry a word of encouragement. He had hoped he was on the right track. There were times when he was sure, and then there were times when he would wonder. Now he knew he was right.

Henry went back to Detroit to work with a vengeance on his second car. It was two feet longer than the first. It could go backward as well as forward. He puttered with pistons, experimented in spark timing and number of revolutions per minute. The crankshaft made a complete revolution on a single power impulse. Henry figured that two impulses, properly placed, would increase both the power and the smoothness of the running. There were many other things to think about, too. He would have to get money to start a factory. He would have to get people interested, and then get them to believe in his horseless carriages and buy them. His job was just beginning.

PART THREE

1901-1915

Part 3
1901-1915

CHAPTER II

THE WHISTLE BLEW and the conductor shouted, "All aboard." Henry stood on the station platform and waved good-bye to his family. Clara was taking Edsel to visit his grandparents in Dearborn.

Henry would miss them. It wasn't pleasant to come home to an empty house, but it was good for the boy to know farm life, and Clara and Edsel did get so much pleasure planning each trip weeks in advance. Clara had begged Henry to come along, but these were such busy days for him.

He had worked on his second car eight years. He was still with the Edison Company. Now he was chief engineer, making over $100 a month, which was a big advancement from the $45 a month he had received when he started to work for the company.

In his free time Henry tried to interest men with

financial means in his plans. It was a discouraging strug-
gle. "How's the great inventor coming?" they would
laugh as he walked into their offices.

One said, "Even if I let you have the money to manufacture this contraption, who do you think would buy it?
Too much of a gamble for me."

Another said, "Great guns, Ford, you've got a gold
mine. We'll float a big company, sell stock, build a big
phaeton for the fellows who can pay three or four thousand for it. We'll make about three or four hundred percent on each car."

Building a car was only half of Henry's idea, and building it cheaply was the other half. The rich men could
buy the big phaetons — he wanted to build a machine the
common folks like himself could afford to buy.

The names of Winton, Duryea, Olds, Haynes, and
Apperson were becoming widely known as automobile
manufacturers. They were followed by Peerless, Cadillac,
Studebaker, and Marmon.

Thoughts about finding men with money who would
listen to his plans were hammering in Henry's head when
he left the railroad station. His little car chug-chugged
up the street. Already he was missing Clara, for he liked
to talk over his ideas with her. He decided to stop at
Coffee Jim's lunch wagon, where he could get friendly
cheer as well as a cup of good coffee.

Coffee Jim was alone, standing behind a pan heaped
with hamburger. "Well, well, glad to see you, Henry,"
Coffee Jim said. "Any news about the money for your
factory?"

Henry shook his head and slid up on a stool. "No, not

yet, but I haven't given up," Henry said hopefully. "You see, it takes longer for a fellow who works for a salary and doesn't have influential friends."

"Can't understand it. Why, there ain't a harder worker, nor a more honest man in Detroit!" Coffee Jim boomed.

"Thanks, you're a good friend. But the ones with money to invest want to use me for a puppet. If I could get them to see over their noses and follow my ideas, everything would be all right."

"You've got a good upper story." Coffee Jim chuckled as he tapped his head with his knuckles. "You'll figure a way to make them see over their big noses. What'll you have? Coffee?"

Henry stirred his coffee. "I do have an idea, but it's the same old thing, money, money, money."

"What's in your noodle now?"

"Well, you know the country is wild about racing — bicycle racing, horse racing, any kind of racing. If I could just build a racing car and enter her in the races next year, she'd open the eyes of these fellows." The very thought of his car winning a race and what it would mean made Henry's heart pound wildly.

"You mean you want to build racing cars?"

"No, no, Coffee Jim, if I could build something good enough to win a race, don't you see, people would have faith in my ability, and I wouldn't have any trouble getting the money to build my cars."

"You could build the blame racer?"

"Sure thing, if I had the time and money. It would be a cinch. But even if I did rake up enough money for

material, if I just worked evenings I wouldn't have it
ready for years. Still I can't afford to give up my job.
I've got a wife and son to support.

Coffee Jim nodded. "You got a fine wife and a smart
kid. Your wife gives me good cake when I come up to
the shed to watch you work." Then he was silent for a
long time. Finally, he said, "I've just been thinking
about the money I take to the bank — no wife and kids to
save for. You quit your job, build the car and race. I'll
stake you."

"You will?" Henry couldn't believe his ears. He
jumped up and shook Coffee Jim's hand vigorously. "I'll
build a racer that will make their eyes pop out," he said
enthusiastically.

The next day Henry quit his job and started to work
on the racer. He built a compact two-cylinder engine and
assembled a skeleton chassis. A few trial runs convinced
him that it would go like the wind. He promptly challenged Alexander Winton, who had won the track cham-
pionship of the United States with his racer, The Bullet.
The race was arranged at the Grosse Pointe track near
Detroit, which was one of the best known tracks in the
country.

Henry spent long hours designing, figuring out problems of air-resistance and weight. Early in the summer
of 1902, after eight months of work, Henry's racer was
ready for a real test. Coffee Jim squeezed into the pilot's
seat with Henry and they took it out at four o'clock one
morning when everyone was off the street.

Coffee Jim held on to his hat with both hands. "The

buzzard goes like a streak of lightning," he wheezed, struggling for his breath.

Henry laughed. "This isn't anything to what she'll do when she gets on the track. We'll beat this all to smash!"

The Grosse Pointe races caused no end of excitement. There was an enormous crowd. The newspapers described the spectators as "society folks" from Detroit and Cleveland. They had come to see the great champion, Winton. Winton was cheered wildly. He sat waiting, swanky and confident, in his car which had broken all records.

Then Henry drove his crude contraption out on the track. There were a few straggly cheers. People joked about his funny car and asked who this man Ford from Detroit was. Coffee Jim was there to slap Henry's shoulder. "Give her everything she's got, like you told me that morning at four o'clock!" he said.

The great bicycle champion, Tom Cooper, was there to see the big show. He walked out on the track to talk with Winton. The crowd gave him hilarious cheers.

"Sort of a pushover for you today, Winton, with only that dinky car of Ford's for competition?" Cooper asked.

"Yeh," Winton said smugly, "I don't expect to have to open her up."

Clara and Edsel were in the grandstand waiting tensely for the pistol shot that would send the racers on their way. Clara's anxiety was mixed with fear that Henry might lose the race, and fear that she might lose her husband. Automobile racing, she thought, was a mighty dangerous sport.

The great Winton stood up in his car, waved his cap to

the cheering crowd, and settled back in The Bullet. Henry waited quietly for the signal. The piercing shot came and the race was on.

The Bullet shot out on the track and Henry's car leaped after it. The Winton was holding an easy lead through the first, second, and into the third stretch. The crowd shouted wildly for Winton. Clara clenched her hands and bit her lips. Edsel shouted at the top of his voice, "Give her the gas, Dad!" Coffee Jim strained his lungs shrieking, "Ford, Ford, come on, Henry!"

The little car was working up closer to the rear of the Winton. Closer and closer it moved — then Henry shot ahead of the champion.

It was a great shock to the audience and the waiting world to learn that the man named Henry Ford had lowered the national automobile record for a mile to one minute, one and one-fifth seconds, and was now declared track champion of the United States.

Tom Cooper, the well-known bicycle racer, rushed up to Henry. Henry was sitting in his little car wiping the dust and perspiration from his face. "Congratulations, Ford," Cooper said, "what a race!"

Cooper looked the car over carefully. "Whose engine did you use?" he asked.

"I made it."

"The deuce you made it! Well, I'll be switched. I'd like to come out and have a look at it one of these days."

"Come any time. Glad to show it to you."

For the next few days Henry was very busy with reporters and photographers. Newspapers flashed pictures of Henry, his car and the old shed across the front page. They printed accounts of his work and his desire to organize a company. Henry was swamped with offers — but it was the same old story, they all insisted that Henry accept their terms as to what kind of a car he would build. And Henry stuck to his idea that manufacturers should put their product within reach of the greatest possible number of people to do the greatest public service.

Frequently Tom Cooper stopped at the old shed. Henry and Tom were becoming close friends. Sometimes they sat on the front porch and talked about ways to get the money under Henry's terms. "Why not win another race?" Cooper suggested one night. "There will be another at Grosse Pointe Track next spring."

"If I use the same car they wouldn't see anything different or startling. Say — hold on — if I could build a new car — "

"Sure! That's it!" Cooper became enthusiastic too. "Can you make a better one?" he asked eagerly.

"I've got a four cylinder one in my head that would be a ripsnorter!"

Cooper jumped to his feet and slapped Henry on the shoulder. "Go to it!" he shouted. "I'll back you and the sky's the limit!"

Henry had never had an offer like this before, and he could scarcely believe his ears. "Man — what I can do with an offer like that! I'm starting to work with my pencil and paper this minute. The design is in my head already," Henry said as he shook hands with Cooper.

With no limit on funds, Henry started to work on two cars for speed only. The motors had four large cylinders which developed eighty horsepower. This was more than anyone had ever thought of in connection with an automobile. The little shed vibrated when the motors were turned on.

Henry called one "999" after the famous engine of the

Empire State Express, and the other the "Arrow." He decided on "999" to run the spring Grosse Pointe race. Henry was sure his racer would be as famous as the powerful steam locomotive.

Cooper was dumbfounded when they took it out on the track. The motor roar was deafening; it could be heard for blocks. Henry drove it around the track. Cooper watched in awe.

"That's only half of what she can do. I didn't open her up. What do you think of the '999'?" Henry asked with a twinkle in his eye.

"Good Lord, man, you don't think I'm going to drive that rocket?" Cooper said, shaking his head. "Not for all the tea in China!"

"Nor I," Henry retorted. "What good is it without a driver? There isn't a man alive that would risk his life with it."

"It looks as if you've sure built a racer! But what are we going to do about a driver? There must be somebody loony enough to believe he has nine lives. Say — wait a minute —— " Cooper snapped his fingers. "I know a daredevil bicycle rider who is a speed maniac. We'll wire him. His name is Barney Oldfield. He's our man!"

Young Oldfield was a professional bicycle rider. He

had never driven an automobile but the thought of a new speed thrill intrigued him.

Barney arrived a week before the appointed date for the race. Henry and Cooper jammed every detail of driving and mechanics into Oldfield that week. He learned about the motor, how to handle the heavy tiller, how to take the curves safely. Barney took the car out on the track the day before the race and drove it around at low speed.

He was as much at home with the "999" as he was with his bicycle. "I'll handle her all right. Tomorrow I'll give her all she's got," he said.

Grosse Pointe Track was a three mile track with un-banked curves. There were six cars entered in the race. Oldfield was steady as a sphinx. "This lalapaloza may kill me, but she won't be crawling when she does!" Barney told Cooper while Henry was cranking the "999."

They were off! Outwardly Oldfield looked as cool as a cucumber, but inside he was bubbling like an active volcano. The "999" reached top speed and flames leaped into the air. Oldfield took the unbanked curves without trying to shut off the engine. If he had any thoughts of crashing to a pulp, he was intensely enjoying his last ride. The "999" finished more than a half mile ahead of

the next car. Barney Oldfield and the "999" were talked about from coast to coast.

A few weeks later Oldfield took the "999" to Yonkers, New York, and added new laurels for himself and Henry. Barney was thrilled with his new career. Bicycle racing was much too tame for him now.

Henry was happy with the record of his racer, not because he was enthusiastic about automobile racing, but because it would be the means of accomplishing his plans. He knew he must strike while the "999" was in the news. He pondered over his possibilities. There was Alexander Malcolmson, a coal dealer, who had shown more than casual interest in the possibilities of a future for the horseless carriage. Henry had bought coal from him while working for the Edison Company. Malcolmson had visited his shed and ridden in his car. He decided to see Malcolmson in the morning.

The FORDMOBILE

The Latest and Best

with detachable tonneau

$850.00

JRT

CHAPTER 12

"GOOD MORNING, ALEX," Henry called as he walked into Malcolmson's office.

"What's on your mind, Henry?" Malcolmson asked, after Henry had exchanged a few words with the clerk, James Couzens, who was seated at the high desk in the corner.

"Alex, one day you said you thought the time was coming when people would be interested in automobiles. Any chance that you might like to be a pioneer in manufacturing a motorcar?"

"Well, you've kind of made people sit up and take notice with the '999,'" Malcolmson said as he chewed on his cigar and shifted it to the other side of his mouth. He had already made up his mind he was going to put some of his money in automobile stock, but he didn't know whether Henry was his man or not. Finally, he said, "What's the deal, Henry?"

James Couzens listened at his desk with his ears perked up like a rabbit's.

"We'll place a light, efficient car on the market that can be sold for less than $1,000, under the name of the Ford Motor Company."

"There's a carpenter shop down here on Mack Avenue that can be remodeled into an automobile factory. I'll take on the responsibility of general manager and chief engineer at $200 a month."

"What kind of a shake do I get on the stock?" Malcolmson asked.

"We'll be equal owners of 51 percent of the stock in a $100,000 company — you'll own 25½ percent of the stock and I'll own 25½ percent." Henry knew Malcolmson could raise the money. "You'll guarantee all bills of the company up to $3,000."

Malcolmson was silent for a long time. All his life he had been looking for a chance to make "big money." His coal business was successful, but he had his eye on bigger business, and he wondered if this was his opportunity.

"Go ahead with your plans," Malcolmson said at last, "I'm with you!" He turned to his clerk, James Couzens, "Got any money you want to invest?" he asked. "I've known Henry for a long time and I know that he could have gone to the top of the Edison Company. And I don't figure he'd have thrown away that chance if he hadn't had something better up his sleeve."

Couzens had been waiting for this moment. He had talked to Henry many times about his idea to build an inexpensive car. Couzens knew Henry was honest, and smart about machines. "I've got $900 in the bank and

HENRY FORD, ENGINEER

$1500 in notes I'd like to invest. And you can count on

"Since you're so keen about this venture, Couzens, it
might be wise if I gave you money to deposit in your

"Why?" Henry and Couzens asked at the same time.

"Well, my credit at the bank might not be so good if

Henry realized an automobile business was not con-
"I just heard of two fellows, Orville and Wilbur Wright,
who are crazier than I am. They're trying to make a

"Now, just imagine any man sinking his money into

"You won't go wrong on our deal, boys," Henry said
build one that will meet the needs of the multitude! I'll
make a buggy that will go without a horse, and make it
so cheap that those who cannot afford a horse and buggy

Henry's heart was light as a feather as he left the coal
office. He was actually going to get started on his big

It was early fall before the business really got under
way. There were so many things to be worked out. They

according to Henry's designs, from different manufacturers, and assemble the automobiles in the factory on Mack Street. Henry wished they had the money to construct instead of purchasing parts, which would reduce cost and insure uniform quality. But this was impossible now. That would have to come later.

Henry worked long hours. The car would have two cylinders and develop eight horsepower. It would go thirty miles an hour. He went to see the two Dodge brothers, who ran a machine shop in Detroit, about making parts for 650 cars at the rate of ten cars a day. The Dodge brothers would take fifty shares of stock in the company in exchange for their work. This was a considerable gamble for the brothers for they had many offers from other companies already established. But they had a hunch Henry had something in his small car, in comparison with the expensive car that Olds and other firms put out.

Finally, on June 16, 1903, all the necessary "red tape" was completed, and the company was incorporated with thirteen stockholders.

It was necessary to employ only a few men for the assembling. There was a mechanic, a draftsman, and a general handy man. The wages of these men were less than twenty-five cents per hour, the regular rate. These men worked right along into the night with Henry and cared nothing about watching the clock. Henry was never satisfied with the finished product, and always felt there were ways to improve it.

James Couzens was acting as secretary and treasurer of the Ford Motor Company. By the middle of August, eight or ten cars had been assembled and none shipped.

FORD MOTOR COMPANY

Couzens urged Henry to ship the cars and get the money. "We've only a small working capital and it's getting low!" Couzens warned Henry.

Henry reluctantly took the cars to the freight train, crated them, and sent them on their way to Minneapolis, St. Paul and Indianapolis.

A few newspapers and trade journals carried articles which described the Ford car. They said the car Henry Ford was building was especially made for everyday wear and tear. Its low price was arranged to place it within the reach of the man of moderate means. It was simple enough so that the average person, even though not a mechanic, could run it.

Within a year there were substantial orders and Couzens's records showed a net profit of $36,957.64. The little Ford wasn't doing too badly. People all over the country were just catching on to the great adventure of motoring. "Have you seen the new Ford?" was the question that leaped across America.

The Ford sold for $850, but the lamps, horn, and windshield were extra. Other motorcars were selling up to $8000, so anything below $1000 was indeed good news for the people with modest bank accounts.

"Do you suppose people will ever discard their good horses and fine bicycles for these noisy, rattly animal scarers?" was another question asked in every social gathering and on street corners.

The few people who had discovered that motoring was fun were having a wonderful time. Papa would put on his goggles, and linen duster to protect him from the dust, and crank his "galloping hessian" with gusto. Mama would tie her long veil around her large straw hat, fasten

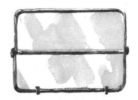

her similar linen duster and sit erectly beside Papa. They
flew like Pegasus across the rough country roads at the
daring speeds of twenty miles an hour, while the children joggled in the back seat like popcorn kernels in a
skillet.

They would carry several inner tubes and extra
casings, a good supply of spark plugs, and enough tools
to supply a machine shop. Cranking the engine was not
always easy. Sometimes the crank spun round and round
and nothing happened. With persistent effort the ulti-
mate result was either a wrenched arm or a lusty cloud of
smoke. If there were hills in the tour, the gears might
slip, and down to the bottom they descended only to try
the ascension over and over. If it rained, the gay adven-
turers were drenched by the time they got out and solved
the puzzle of just where each rain curtain belonged, for

they were of different sizes and shapes.

Henry was pleased to learn of the organization of the United States Office of Public Roads, which succeeded the Office of Road Inquiry. The new department ordered a census of the nation's main roads. The country was showing a real interest in good roads. This trend, Henry knew, would help his little car to take the place of horses and bicycles. There were experiments with concrete as a substance for roads. In 1904 a mile or so of concrete paving was laid in four or five scattered towns. If roads improved, Henry knew that interest in motoring would flourish.

The Ford cars numbered 1708 the first year. The people who bought them were the most venturesome type, who were willing to crawl under their cars when the temperamental motor would grow balky.

CHAPTER 13

HENRY WAS FORTY years old when he finally got the Ford Motor Company into production. He was glad his little factory on Mack Street had a good start. But when cold weather set in, the sales gradually decreased, and when winter arrived, they practically stopped. Automobile owners found no pleasure trying to cope with snow and ice in rutty roads. The little side curtains weren't much protection from low temperatures, and radiators were constantly freezing. People who owned cars decided it was easier to put them on jacks for the winter months and forget about them until spring. During this time the factory must be kept running to have cars ready for spring sales.

In the spring a new model would have side curtains that rolled up inside and strapped to the top. There would be a collapsible top that could be lowered when the weather was clear.

But meanwhile Henry knew he must do something to keep the Ford name in front of the public. There had been great advertising value in racing. He could do it again with a new angle. He could rebuild his "Arrow" and try to make a record on the ice of Lake St. Clair.

When Henry told Clara about this idea, she was disturbed.

"Henry, this is such a dangerous undertaking," she said. "If you insist upon the 'Arrow' making a speed record on the ice, why not write to Mr. Oldfield and have him drive the racer?"

Henry laughed good-naturedly. "Clara," he said, "you know I only take advice when I agree. This is my idea and I'll see it through."

Clara said no more, but Henry knew she would not have a moment's peace until after January 12, the date set for the exhibition.

The day of the race was cold and blustery, and a raw wind pierced the heaviest clothing.

"Are you sure you'll be warm enough?" Clara asked with great concern as Henry buttoned up his black astrakhan coat.

"Stop worrying about me, Clara," Henry said, impatiently, "I'm sweating like a butcher — I'd be warm in my unionsuit today!"

Clara, Edsel, and Henry scrambled into the Ford and drove the ten miles to the four-mile track out on the lake.

"Papa, can I ride in the 'Arrow' with you, please?" Edsel pleaded.

"Indeed not," Clara answered promptly. "If you say another word about riding in the 'Arrow,' you shall go to bed without any supper."

"I'll take you for a ride in the racer another time," Henry told his son.

"But you won't go as fast as you will today." The promise was little comfort to the ten-year-old Edsel.

When they arrived at the track, Henry couldn't see the "Arrow" and he sensed the uneasy feeling of the crowd.

One of the men from the factory rushed to tell him that the final test had disclosed something wrong with the engine. The mechanics had been working frantically for several hours trying to get the racer into shipshape condition.

The thrill-seeking spectators stamped their feet up and down, and clapped their hands together to beat the numbness from them. Others stood as rigid as birddogs, pointing a covey of quail.

Henry was just getting into his Ford to drive back to the factory when there was a faraway rumble, like thunder. The worried lines disappeared from Henry's face, for even at that distance he could tell that the roar of the motor was right.

"We got her licked, Boss," the mechanic beamed as he turned the "Arrow" over to Henry.

The crowd cheered. Everything was set. "BANG," the pistol cracked and Henry was off.

Clara lowered her eyes only to raise them again to see the "Arrow" skid and leap like a bucking bronco. The ice that looked so smooth was full of fissures. Each fissure sent the racer careening into the air, and down with a thud, teetering for its balance.

The crowd shrieked and screamed.

"Faster, Papa, faster!" Edsel shouted. "Gee, I wish I was out there with Papa."

Clara said nothing. She closed her eyes and prayed. She prayed that Henry would come through this alive, and that he would never again do any more racing.

With all his strength Henry clutched the wheel, not knowing when a fissure would send him crashing to the ground.

Miraculously Henry brought the "Arrow" to the finish. "You've done it again!" people cheered as the car stopped. He had broken a world's record, travelling at a pace of ninety-two miles an hour, and setting a new fast time for the mile of thirty-nine and two-fifths seconds. Again Henry and his racer carried headlines all over the country.

That evening Clara and Henry discussed the triumph. "It is just too risky," Clara said. "What would be gained if you lost your life? You are doing this only to further your plans, and there would be no one to go on with your great ideas."

This time Henry agreed with Clara. His experience had been much more dangerous than he had anticipated.

However, he went to sleep happily satisfied with his per-
forming "Arrow." But little could he suspect that he
would face a major problem in the morning.

The next day Jim Couzens met Henry at the door of
the factory. "Henry, I couldn't tell you last week when
you were all keyed up about the race, but we can't meet
the pay roll."

Henry's heart sank. "If the men quit," he said, "we're
through!" He knew he couldn't raise the money from
the stockholders. He didn't want to sell any of his stock,
for if he did he would lose the controlling interest he
held with Malcolmson, and then Malcolmson could be
boss.

"What are you going to do?" Couzens asked.

"There's only one thing to do — put our cards on the
table."

When the men came for their pay checks that evening,
Henry was waiting for them. He stood on a chair so they
could all hear him. He told them honestly just what he
was up against. "If you stick with us, we'll get through
the winter on our unfinished orders," Henry said. "That
little four-cylinder model will be the talk of the country
in the spring. We'll see a phenomenal increase in business. People are beginning to see the advantages in motoring. But if you walk out now — we're all washed up.
How about it, men?"

He waited breathlessly for the decision. What would
the men do? If they walked out, everything he had
accomplished would be smashed.

The men broke up into little groups and mumbled to
each other. Then Henry's face broke into a broad smile,

for he heard: "Sure we'll stay, Chief." Some of the men came up to shake hands with him and tell him of their confidence in him. Their loyalty and friendship warmed his soul. He hoped he could do something for them someday.

CHAPTER 14

SPRING FILLED ALL of Henry's predictions. Orders piled up faster than they could be filled at the Mack Street Shop. The factory was completely inadequate. So Henry built a new factory on Piquette and Beaubien Streets. It was a three story building with new machinery that seemed most satisfactory and looked as if it would take care of their needs forever.

Now that Henry did not have to worry about money matters, he could put some of his ideas in management and manufacturing into effect. The new factory was all paid for out of earnings. Henry paid Coffee Jim and Tom Cooper the money he owed them. Years ago ·when Henry had thought about a watch factory he believed all similar parts should be made with no variation whatsoever. He could now do a bit of this with automobiles. For the first time the company actually manufactured a few parts, but the factory was still chiefly an assembling plant.

Profits were rolling in and the stockholders were happy. Henry was keeping his eye on the figures, as well as the other angles, and was particularly disturbed to discover the company had made more money, and employed more men, but sold less cars proportionately per model. This did not fit Henry's idea of the greatest good for the greatest number.

Malcolmson was very pleased with the way things were going. He liked his big dividend check. He held just as much stock as Henry, which meant he had just as much to say about the voting policies of the company. "If I could just get Malcolmson's stock," Henry thought, "the other stockholders would go along with me. That man is like a noose around my neck!"

The next year when there was still a slight drop in cars sold, Henry was determined to get Malcolmson's stock no matter what the price. He wanted to run things his way and do away with controversial ideas at stockholders' meetings. Malcolmson had made an original investment of $3,000; now he valued his stock at $175,000!

This was a staggering sum, but Henry knew he must have the stock. He borrowed the money and gave notes to buy it. Henry now owned 510 shares of stock; the original 255 shares of his own and Malcolmson's 255 shares, which gave him the controlling interest of 51 percent.

Soon the company turned out one hundred cars in a day. The newspapers called it a world's record. This was four times more than any other builder was making. When Henry said he looked forward to making a thousand cars a day, his associates were worried.

The remaining stockholders asked each other if the man was completely crazy. They did not know that Henry was planning to assemble cars a new way.

October 1, 1908, Henry introduced his new wonder model. The new Model T caused such a sensation the stockholders did not dare to cross him. It was designed with features no one had ever thought of. People actually fought to own one.

The driver's wheel was on the left side instead of the right so drivers could see what they were passing. It was no longer necessary to climb under the car to repair the motor. The top was removable. It could be unbolted and lifted off.

All the cylinders had been made at one time out of a single engine block. They had been manufactured separately and then welded together. Henry's new idea was called the removable cylinder head. It permitted equal compression in all cylinders.

Henry wanted his cars to have a reputation for standing up. He wanted them to be tough, simple, and well made. A new vanadium steel was used in the Model T which made a lighter and much stronger car. Henry came across this important material almost by accident. Up until this time he had known he lacked the secret to give strength without weight.

In 1905 Henry had gone to a motor race at Palm Beach, and entered one of his cars. There was a big smashup and a French car was wrecked. As Henry observed the foreign cars, he thought they had smaller and better parts than American manufacturers knew anything about. After the wreck he picked up a little valve strip stem. It was very light and very strong. He asked what it was made of, but nobody knew. He gave the stem to his assistant.

"Find out all about this," Henry ordered. "That is the kind of material we ought to have in our cars."

Eventually, Henry learned that it was a French steel and that there was vanadium, a rare silver-white metallic element in it.

Henry contacted every steelmaker in America. Not one could make vanadium steel. Henry then sent to England for a man who understood how to make the steel commercially. The next thing was to get a plant to turn it out, and that was a real problem. Vanadium required 3,000 degrees Fahrenheit. The ordinary furnace could not go beyond 2,700 degrees. Henry found a small company in Canton, Ohio. He offered to guarantee them against loss if they would run a heat for him. They agreed. The first heat was a failure. Very little vanadium remained in the steel. He begged them to try again. The second time the steel came through. Henry was jubilant. He knew he would be able to increase the strength of his car threefold with the new steel.

As soon as the new vanadium was produced, Henry pulled apart one of his Fords and tested it in detail to determine what kind of steel was best for every part. Some parts needed a hard steel, a tough steel, or an elastic steel. After the testing Henry selected twenty different types of steel for the various steel parts. About ten of these were vanadium. Vanadium was used wherever strength and lightness were required.

Each Model T owner received a manual which pictured the construction of the car and gave clear, simple instructions about upkeep and repairs. It didn't take a mechanical genius to repair a Ford. The parts cost so little it was just as economical to buy new ones as to repair the old ones. The touring car sold for $850, and the roadster for $825.

America named the car "flivver," and it was sometimes called "tin lizzie." Some people thought it was so light and flimsy it would shake to pieces on the rough roads. Henry only laughed at this criticism, and said it would be easy to prove that they were wrong. And he did.

It was June 1, 1909. For weeks the papers had been full of an exciting event that was to take place on that date. Before the New York City Hall, five "horseless carriages," an Acme, a Shawmut, an Itala, and two Model T Fords stood hub to hub. Mechanics were hurrying to make final adjustments. Then, from the White House, President Taft flashed the starting signal. America's first transcontinental auto race was under way.

West of St. Louis seven-day rains had turned the country roads into quagmires. Across the prairies and in Colorado average speeds were cut to ten miles an hour.

At Cheyenne, Wyoming, the big Itala quit the race. The others plowed on. Near the summit of the Cascades they fought their way against towering snowdrifts.

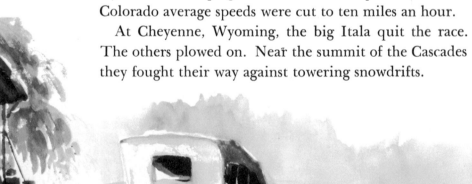

Days later, Ford Car Number 2, the winner, entered the gates of Seattle's Alaska-Yukon-Pacific Exposition. It had crossed the continent in 22 days and 55 minutes, with New York air still in the two front tires!

As Colonel M. Robert Guggenheim awarded the cup, he said: "Mr. Ford's theory that a lightweight car, highly powered, can go places where heavier cars cannot go, and beat heavier cars costing five and six times as much on the steep hills or on bad roads has been proved. I believe Mr. Ford has the solution to the problem of the popular automobile."

The Model T had not shaken to pieces! Henry immediately announced that they would discontinue all their other models and concentrate on Model T. The Model T, mounted high over four wheels, with a little black box out front that hid, but in no way silenced a four-cylinder motor, made Henry famous and wealthy, and put America on wheels.

A farmer could jack up the right rear wheel of his Model T and belt a pulley to a buzz saw and begin cutting the winter's supply of logs. The next day he might use the Model T as a power plant to grind corn for his horses and his cows. And on Sunday he would take the Missus to church in that same Model T.

There were many jokes about the Model T, and Henry

enjoyed each new one he heard. He thought they were good advertising. Even children loved the little jingles like these:

> A little spark, a little coil,
> A little gas, a little oil,
> A piece of tin, a two inch board —
> Put them together and you have a Ford.
>
> There was an old man
> And he had a wooden leg;
> A ride he couldn't steal,
> A ride he couldn't beg.
> So he got four spools
> And an old tin can,
> Built himself a Ford,
> And the darn thing ran.

Learning to drive a Model T required no special genius. In front was a crank that either started the motor or broke your arm. It had a "planetary" transmission, with three pedals for your feet. To get it on its way you pulled down the brass lever under the steering wheel to the right, speeded up the motor, and stepped on the pedal at the left. Then invisible wheels ground and ground, the motor complained, the body shook and shivered, and finally the Model T moved ahead.

When the car started, you let up on the pedal and jerked into high gear. The contraption leaped like a horse stung by a bee. To stop, you pushed hard on the pedal at the right. The one in the middle was the reverse pedal. Then you pulled on the hand brake, which threw the car into neutral.

You had neither lights nor horn unless the motor was running. There was no door on the left — only a panel

AFFECTIONATELY DRAWN
BY JOSHUA TOLFORD

that looked like a door. You either climbed over the side from the left or preceded your passenger in from the right.

Gasoline was fed by gravity to the carburetor from a tank under the front-seat. To fill the tank everybody had to pile out and the cushion had to be removed.

Carbon was a great nuisance too. The wearing of the sidewalls of the pistons or cylinders allowed the lubricating oil to get into the combustion chamber and built up a sooty deposit known as carbon. When the motor carboned to a point where the knock was like the beat of a sledgehammer, the owner who was mechanically minded would unbolt the cylinder head, scrape off the carbon with his pocketknife, put the head back on and be on his way.

When the connecting-rod bearings achieved more than a quarter of an inch play and the motor sounded like a boiler factory, the owner crawled underneath, took off the oil pan, and relined the bearing with whatever was at hand — a piece from an old tin can or old shoe leather.

Less than six months after the model was introduced the entire output of the factory was spoken for — the Ford had outgrown another factory.

JRT

CHAPTER 15

H ENRY'S HOME LIFE was pleasant and happy. Clara lived for her husband and her son. She was never cross when Henry was late and the dinner would get cold. She knew that if Henry were interested in something he was doing, the dinnerhour would go by and he would forget about eating. But Clara never allowed Edsel to have late meals. He had his meals on the dot.

Sometimes Henry would come home and work hard on some problem until twelve or one o'clock. It wouldn't seem fair to Clara to go to bed, so she would sew or read until Henry was tired and ready to sleep.

Clara and Henry were devoted to Edsel. He was a handsome dark-haired youth. Of course, Henry was pleased as Punch when Edsel showed mechanical interests, at a very early age, and wanted to build engines with him in his workshop.

When Edsel was just three, Henry perched him on the lid of the battery box of his car and they drove about Detroit. With cheeks flushed from the wind and excitement, Edsel would shout, "Faster, faster, Papa."

While Henry reveled in Edsel's mechanical interest, Clara saw another side to his nature. He had an exceptional talent for painting, which Clara praised and encouraged. She believed it was a fine thing for a young boy to understand and appreciate art. Often they visited the Detroit Institute of Arts where Edsel enjoyed the works of the great masters.

One evening when Edsel was going to high school Henry found him working at the library desk, poring over a stack of books.

"When did you turn into a bookworm?" Henry laughed.

"Gee, these are interesting books, Dad — look, here's one on Fulton, and this one's on Stephenson and the story of the steam locomotive."

"Those are the things I wanted to read about when I was a boy," Henry said with a note of remorse in his voice, remembering how he had longed to know about steam engines and machinery.

"I have to turn in a theme tomorrow so I chose 'Transportation.' Listen and see how it sounds, will you?"

"A fine subject. Let's have it," Henry said as he slumped into an easy chair and crossed his legs.

Edsel picked up his papers and read:

"When man realized the folly of depending only on shank's mare and reached out for better transportation, the dawn of better days was here. Transportation, by sea and land, has been man's problem since the beginning of time.

"The first travelling on the sea was done on a floating log. Next the logs were linked to form a raft. Then the hollowed log and on to Fulton's 'Clermont.' Today we have great ocean carriers.

"On land the beast of burden was man's first carrier. Then came the first wheeled vehicles — the crude disc cut from a tree, attached to a pole.

"From Pharaoh's chariot to the prairie schooner of our pioneer days with a thousand kinds in between, all depended for power on beasts.

"In the early days of America and up to the first years of the last century, travel on horseback and by stage was very slow, difficult and even dangerous. In 1811 the average time, by stage, between New York and Philadelphia (a distance of ninety miles) was twenty-six hours!

"Then came steam power. The names of Watt, Trevithick, and Stephenson will always be honored by schoolboys and statesmen. The pioneers in the great job of harnessing steam saw a system of mechanical transport for the United States that would spread over the land like a great web. They predicted that speeds of thirty, fifty, and even a hundred miles an hour would someday be practicable.

"The automobile will serve our swiftly growing country as a necessary means of transportation. It will bring great changes in our future mode of living. And while the automobile satisfies human wants on the ground, our newest infant, the airplane, will blaze a pathway through the air."

Edsel folded his paper and waited for his father's comment.

"By Jove, that's all right," Henry said, nodding his head. He had a feeling of satisfaction that Edsel would be competent to carry on his great business in the years ahead. "By the way, how's that plane coming?" Henry added.

Edsel was assisting three men in building the first Ford airplane. The factory was a barn at the rear of 1302 Woodward Avenue, rented for the purpose by Henry. Most of the machine work was done at the Ford Motor Company, then located at the Piquette plant.

"She's going to be a beauty, Dad!" Edsel beamed with enthusiasm. "Boy, oh boy, you should hear that motor hum."

Henry was pleased that Edsel was interested in mechanical progress. Since the day Henry heard about the Wright Brothers trying to build a machine that would fly in the air like a bird, he had watched the development of aviation with great interest.

The first Ford plane which Edsel helped build was a single place, high wing, externally braced monoplane powered by a direct drive Ford Model T engine, developing 28 horsepower. Like many planes it was equipped with a tricycle landing gear.

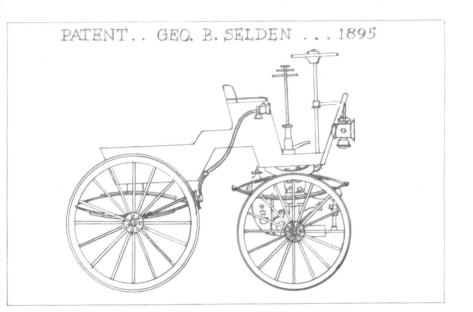

CHAPTER 16

EVERYTHING SEEMED TO be going fine at the factory until Henry found himself involved in a lawsuit. One morning a policeman appeared and served Henry with papers. A group of automobile manufacturers were prosecuting him for violating the Selden patent.

Selden, who was a patent attorney, had acquired a patent in 1895 for producing "a safe, simple, and cheap road locomotive, light in weight, easy to control, possessed of sufficient power to overcome ordinary inclination." Meanwhile, Selden did nothing about producing such a vehicle, but the other inventors who produced motorcars formed an association and acquired a license to use the Selden patent. It was this association that brought suit against the Ford Motor Company.

The members of the organization paid a royalty to the

Electric Vehicle Company on every car built by them because the Electric Vehicle Company had secured the rights to the Selden patent.

"We'll put you out of business if you don't join the association," members told Henry.

Henry worried about the lawsuit. He knew it was a serious problem. If he held out, it would mean fighting the entire automobile industry. He would be talked about as being queer. He might even be stopped from making cars altogether. On the other hand, he would not join an association that could tell him how many cars he could make and what he could charge for them. He did not want to pay $15 on every car he made, part of which would go to the association and the rest to the Electric Vehicle Company.

He thought about his first car. He had not known about the Selden patent when he built it. Selden never manufactured cars, but when others did, he accused them of infringing upon his rights. Henry knew his car differed in principle from the engine protected by the Selden patent. Selden's engine was a low compression, low speed mechanism.

"I'll fight it to the last ditch!" Henry told his stockholders with grim determination.

He got the best lawyers he could get and told them to get busy on the case. After several years of battle the fight ended in 1911. Henry won a complete victory in the Court of Appeals. The other automobile manufacturers were as jubilant as Henry. It meant their royalties could stop at once. Members of the association who had been Henry's enemies were the first to praise him for the fight he made. Henry was free to develop his business.

Even the most near-sighted stockholder could see that the Ford Motor Company had outgrown the Piquette plant. Henry purchased a 276 acre site in the northern part of Detroit in the Highland Park district. Buildings for a much larger factory covering forty-seven acres were in progress.

Ever since Henry was a mechanic in the Flower Machine Shop he had believed a factory could and should be a clean place to work. Now cleanliness was the first thing he considered in his new model plant. Plate glass walls made the workrooms light. The buildings were well ventilated and easy to keep clean. A staff of five hundred men was employed to do nothing but sweep floors, wash windows, and look after all sanitary conditions. Twenty-five painters were employed to keep walls and ceilings freshly painted.

The old idea of the watch factory came back: the 1800 men working in the new plant must be organized to do work quickly and efficiently, without loss of motion, to cut the cost of production. Saving steps meant saving money. By saving money the costs to the consumer could be reduced.

Each part of the Ford car would be made in a single department, and every part carried swiftly, by gravity, to the assembling room. The first endless floor conveyor and chain was installed in 1911. Take the work to the men rather than the men to the work, was the basic principle of Henry's new idea — the great assembly line. The

tools and the men would be ready for each part or material as the mechanical carriers moved it on its way. There would be one movement for each man, to reduce thought and unnecessary movements in the new system.

Visitors and other automobile manufacturers came to see the beautiful new buildings and this new idea, "the assembly lines."

The assembly lines looked like a network of railways. Each workman stood at his appointed place ready to do his job, ranging from inserting a small bolt to the fitting of the body on the chassis. The Model T grew, piece by piece, along the moving platforms.

All machines were as foolproof as possible. Each one was thoroughly tested to make sure it was safe. If an accident did occur, Henry made every investigation to prevent the same mishap.

There were criticisms that the monotony in the worker's movements would be injurious to his health. Doctors were hired by the company to detect physical strain. But it was only rarely that a man asked to be shifted to another kind of work, and then he was transferred as soon as possible.

Henry called the men of his employment bureau to him. "If we can employ physically handicapped people,

we are doing our country a service. These crippled and blind people will be self-respecting citizens. We don't need testimonials from men when they are hired — if a man has a prison record and he is willing to work," Henry said,"he will have his chance to make a new life for himself."

Henry's new problem was a great fortune doubling and doubling again. He was a self-made millionaire, and as smart about money as he was about mechanics. "There are two fools in this world," he said, "one is the millionaire who thinks that by hoarding money he can somehow accumulate real power, and the other is the penniless reformer who thinks that if only he can take the money from one class and give it to another, all the world's ills will be cured. They are both on the wrong track."

Henry looked at his vast accumulation of wealth as a farmer looks at his seed corn and saw the beginning of a new and richer harvest. There was something sacred about a big business which provides a living for hundreds and thousands of families. Henry thought about the babies coming into these homes, the boys and girls going to school, the young workingmen who, on the strength of their jobs, were marrying and starting new homes, the thousands of homes that were being paid for on installments out of the earnings of men. The Ford Motor Company was enabling all these things to be done — the continuance and growth of that company was a holy trust to Henry.

As Henry pictured his men and his industry his thoughts turned to earlier days. He had worked shoulder to shoulder with the hired men on the farm at Dearborn.

He had worked shoulder to shoulder with the mechanics in the machine shops of Detroit. He knew his machines from A to Z, and he knew that every screw and nut was necessary to make the machine a successful unit. He knew his men were necessary to make the factories a success. He remembered the promise he had made when he could not meet the pay roll.

For a long time Henry had been concerned about the welfare of his workers. He wondered how they lived when they left the factory — what their homes were like. He assigned two hundred men from his factory to investigate the living conditions of the 15,000 Ford workers. It took a year to make the survey. Henry was shocked by the report. One-fourth of his men were living in poverty with their families, and another one-fourth in only fair condition, and only 364 owned their own homes.

His men were all receiving the standard wage, but if the standard wage was not sufficient for good living, something should be done about it. Henry believed every one of his workmen should earn a comfortable living. He would do something about these wages! The next day was New Year's day, but he called a meeting of the stockholders anyway. A holiday did not stop Henry's plans.

CHAPTER 17

THE STOCKHOLDERS SAT in their regular places around the large table, wondering what was on Henry's mind in calling a meeting New Year's morning.

Henry got up from his chair, walked across the room, and looked out of the second floor office window to the doorway of the employment department. A long line of men waited in the bitter cold to file applications for jobs.

"I've called you here today to find out what you think about bettering the welfare of the workers," Henry said.

The men wondered what Henry meant. The employees already had working conditions superior to those in any other factory.

"In regard to hours," Henry continued, "our men work the standard nine hours a day, and receive an average of $2.34 a day, which is on a par with hours and wages all over the country."

111

The heads around the table all nodded in agreement. They couldn't imagine what the Chief was getting at. There had been no dissatisfaction shown among the workmen — they were glad to have jobs.

"If the men work eight hours instead of nine," Henry said, "we could have three shifts instead of two. We could employ at least four thousand more men."

The men agreed. This was a new departure, but they thought it could be handled all right. They were relieved that it wasn't too startling a change of policy.

But Henry wasn't finished; his plan was much more extensive.

"All right," he said, "we've taken care of the hours, now what will we do about wages? How much can we increase the daily wage?"

"Twenty-five cents a day should be a handsome increase," one man suggested.

Henry wrote it down on a blackboard. "Any other suggestions?" he asked.

"I would say we could make it fifty cents a day," another volunteered, sensing that Henry was not satisfied. "That would cost the company seven thousand five hundred dollars a day or more than two million a year," he added.

"Isn't there anyone who thinks we can do better than that?" Henry searched the faces of the stockholders impatiently.

After a long pause someone timorously named a dollar a day. They were all tossing mental figures with many digits. A dollar a day would mean over four million dollars a year. This was surely the stopping place.

But Henry urged them on until he got them up to

two dollars and fifty cents a day. No man in the factory would receive less than five dollars a day.

Most of the men felt that the boss had certainly tumbled off the deep end this time. Only two of the men at the meeting had confidence in Henry and felt that he knew what he was doing. The others felt that doubling a man's salary for an hour less labor could not be good for the company.

Then while the stockholders were grasping the significance of it all, Henry suggested that ten million dollars more be divided among the employees as a bonus.

The stockholders gasped.

"If the workmen are well paid, I believe they will do just as much work in eight hours as they will do in nine," Henry said. "Besides, it is about time that management shared some of the profits with labor. It is only right that the workmen share the wealth they have helped create."

As soon as the newspapers got the news of the new Ford profit-sharing plan, it was the sensation of the nation. Henry's plan was discussed at every dinner table in the country, on street corners, and every public gathering. Henry Ford was a hero! He was the workingman's friend.

Other automobile manufacturers crumpled their newspapers in disgust. They predicted that Ford would wreck the whole industrial world. It was a bombshell dropped in their midst. One manufacturer said, "Ford isn't satisfied to give those laborers a spotless palace to work in. Now he throws his money at them for coming to work. You can't run a business that way. He'll drive us all into bankruptcy, if we have to compete with his ideas."

Henry had them all worried. Five dollars a day was phenomenal. There was bound to be unrest and dissatisfaction in other plants. Workers hurried to the Ford factory to crowd into the lines pushing in front of the buildings. Everybody wanted to work for the Ford Motor Company.

No one was hired who already had a job. Preference was given to married men out of work. Henry was sorry for the men who had to go back to jobs that did not give them the chance to do their best work because they were not paid enough to keep them healthy and happy.

Henry knew he would have to make his plan work to prove to his competitors that if a worker has the money he needs for his comfort and happiness, it will be better for everybody. He would have to prove to industrial leaders that there were definite values in those things they called impractical — interest and good will. Henry's creed was: Do the thing that is best for everybody and it will be best for you in the end.

His enemies called him a "sentimental idiot," and said his schemes were just for advertising.

After Henry's plan had been tried for many months, he had his two hundred investigators make another survey. The output of cars had increased twenty percent and there was immediate lessened turnover in labor in the Ford plant. The production per man-hour also increased. One Italian workman who made parts increased his production twofold. He explained this by saying, "Mr. Ford pay me two-fifty a day, he get two hundred and fifty pieces. Mr. Ford now pay me five dollars a day, he get five hundred pieces. I pay him back."

Concrete changes in the living conditions of the men had taken place. The report showed that eleven hundred men had moved to better homes. Their bank deposits had increased two hundred and five percent. And more than two million dollars' worth of Detroit real estate had passed into the hands of Ford employees, who were paying for their homes by the month.

This report pleased Henry. He didn't mind if industrial leaders did throw stones at him — he hoped they would have to follow his example and pay higher wages for fewer hours.

CHAPTER 18

"DO YOU KNOW what important day this is, Henry?"
Clara asked as they ate their breakfast of soft boiled
eggs and toast.

"It's July 30. Is it some special day?"

"Indeed it is a special day — your birthday. You're
fifty-two years old today, and I declare I wonder where
you get all your energy. You're a human dynamo!"

Henry's hair was gray, but other than that he was the
same tall, slender man he had been at forty. His eyes
were bright with a zest for living and doing.

"Fifty-two — humph, just the age when folks begin to
get good sense. Well, I feel just as chipper as I did twenty
years ago."

"Well, it seems to me that you should slow up and take
life easier. You've worked so hard."

"Slow up? Why, Clara, I've only started my work."

Clara had learned long ago that it was no use trying to change Henry's mind, and she knew that he would be perfectly miserable sitting around doing nothing. His wiry body and strong mechanic's hands were never weary. She knew that he did not care for society nor conventional forms of entertainment. His entertainment was his work.

"You know," she said, and her eyes had a faraway look, "I remember when I told my mother that Henry Ford would make his mark in this world, but little did I think he would have a million little 'horseless carriages' chugging around the country in 1915."

"Careful how you speak of the Model T, Clara. She doesn't chug — why we don't even have to crank her anymore," Henry said gaily. "She has all kinds of refinements, a generator, a self-starter, a speedometer, a battery, a closed body and glass windows. Why, we keep improving her all the time. The Fords owe a lot to you, Clara. You and I were the assembly line on the first Ford."

"What kind of a wife would I have been if I hadn't stood by my husband?" Clara said indignantly. " A young lady doesn't marry a young man if she doesn't believe in him. But I'm glad I no longer have to make my own hats. They didn't have a bit of style."

JRT

"By George, I certainly think some of those big hats you trimmed and retrimmed were classier than the little dinky ones you buy now!" Henry laughed.

"To get back to your birthday — what would you like for dinner tonight?"

"How about some of that healthful, scientific pie? What do you call it, and how do you make it?"

"You mean my bird's-nest pie? I fill a deep pan with sliced apples, sprinkle them with nutmeg or cinnamon, cover the dish with a sour-cream batter, and put it in the oven to bake. When it's done I turn it into a dish, and the wonderfully browned batter is on the bottom, and the apples heaped on top. It looks just like a bird's nest."

"That's the one. Let's have some of that." Henry got up from the table and was ready to go to the factory.

"Henry," Clara said thoughtfully, "now that you have everything going so well, and Edsel has taken such an interest in the plant, why couldn't we get away for a little while?"

Edsel had gone to work for the company in 1912, the year he finished high school. He was well liked by the men and showed promise of becoming a fine executive.

"Want to take a fancy trip? Where would you like to go?"

"I'd like to go back to the country. We could visit with our old friends and go to square dances." Clara's eyes were as bright as two stars as she thought of recapturing those humble days.

"By jove, I'd like that too," Henry said enthusiastically. "That would give me a fine chance to organize the work on the 1,000 acres adjoining our farm that I just bought. We're going to have a new plant out there.

The River Rouge Plant, that's what it's going to be called, the greatest in the world. And besides I've some unfinished business to do in that old machine shop."

"But I thought I could get you away for a rest," Clara sighed.

"Rest, shucks! Remember that farm locomotive I tried to build years ago? It only ran forty feet. Now I'm going to build a tractor that will run all over the world. I'm going to call it 'The Fordson.'"

❊❊ PART FOUR ❊❊
1915-1941

Part 4
1915 - 1941

CHAPTER 19

HENRY AND CLARA had a wonderful time in Dearborn. They went to square dances and visited with their old friends. While they were there, they decided to build a large stone house on the River Rouge. Clara liked this idea for she had always wanted to come back to Dearborn. She knew that Henry needed the quietness and privacy of a country home. He was now a national figure. He had accomplished things which no other man in the history of industry had accomplished, and constant demands were being made for his ideas, his time and his money.

Henry bought the swampy tract of 1,000 acres, with the Rouge flowing through it, to build a much larger plant than the greatest of automobile plants at Highland Park. He selected this site because of water transportation, the possibilities for expansion, and then too, there was plenty of room for employees to build their homes. The location was desirable for obtaining material. It was about half way between the iron mines of the north, and the southern-central coal mines. Ore could be brought to Dearborn by Ford ore boats on the Great Lakes.

It was during this visit that Henry worked on his farm locomotive and soon was ready to manufacture a light-weight tractor to relieve the farmer of a great many of the laborious farm jobs.

Meanwhile, the European War was worrying the American people. In 1914 the Austrian Archduke Ferdinand and his wife were assassinated. A month later Germany invaded Belgium and Russian armies were marching on Germany. England, France, and Belgium plunged directly into the fire. Four years of trench fighting followed.

The British people needed help. There were not enough horses in Britain to cultivate crops to replace the food sunk by the German submarines. The British had only a few steam tractors, and all the factories were making munitions and war materials. England turned to Henry. Henry let them have his drawings of the tractor, and sent his tractor expert and as many other men to manufacture tractors as they needed. The "Fordson," which was the name Henry gave to his first tractor, was manufactured in England before it was manufactured in the United States.

The war was very disturbing to Henry. He stood staunchly for peace. "The people should realize that they are all bound together as parts of a machine, and anything that hurts one group or nation will eventually hurt the rest of the people," Henry told reporters. War,

Henry thought, was waste in every respect.

Peace workers from neutral countries came to see Henry. They had failed to get the aid of our government so they urged Henry to take the lead in trying to end the war.

Henry's strong desire for peace and his desire to help all the peoples of the world involved him in an expensive experience. He visited President Wilson and pleaded with him to appoint a neutral commission for mediation. Like many others who wanted peace, he failed. Then he thought of another plan. He would charter a ship and with a company of Americans he would go to Europe and put an end to the war.

Henry telephoned Clara from Washington. "We're going to Europe," he said.

"Not I," Clara replied. "We have a son and my duty is to him as well as to you. If anything were to happen to us, Edsel would be alone."

Friends came to Clara and begged her to dissuade Henry from going. But Clara would not interfere. She had learned long ago that Henry must do the thing that seemed right to him. Everything in her was against his going, but she helped him get ready.

One night early in December 1915, in the dark harbor

of New York, a siren shrieked, and the Danish steamer, *Oscar II*, set sail for Europe with Henry and his fellow Americans aboard.

The day was past when Henry's opinions were his private business. Newspapermen were constantly at his heels, and Henry's good will project was misinterpreted. The press ridiculed the boatload of pilgrims sailing into submarine infested waters in an effort to put an end to a war machine. The peace ship was action, drama, and color to news-hungry editors and reporters. Headlines read: "Ford Charters Ark, Plans Raid on Trenches" — "Peace Army Sails for Europe with Auto King as Commander."

Henry's idea had been to open a channel of communications between the enemies. He believed the war was rutted and that the chief powers might exchange views through a neutral agency. "A conference for continuous mediation," Henry thought, could be the machinery to which nations could turn to inquire what could be done to establish peace. The press took every advantage of poking fun at the amateur diplomats, and everyone ignored the "continuous mediation" idea.

Before the ship touched Norway and other European ports Henry realized his purpose could not be fulfilled. Europe was not ready to listen to peace negotiations. The mission failed, but Henry did make his point that the peace idea still existed on earth and millions of peace-loving persons worshipped him for his efforts.

In February 1917, Germany began unrestricted submarine warfare. Two days later the United States broke off diplomatic relations. The training of armies on a huge scale in all our states went into effect with vigor. War was declared on Germany April 6, and thousands of American soldiers were sent to Europe.

Henry offered every facility of his organization to the government without profit. "If the war is to be won," he said, "it will be won by the nation that knows best how to use machinery and tools." Henry's factories made ambulances, trucks, caissons, listening devices, steel helmets, liberty motors for airplanes, and eagle boats for combating submarines.

CHAPTER 20

A S SOON AS the Armistice was signed in 1918, Henry
went back to full production of cars, trucks, and
tractors. The farmer welcomed the tractor with open
arms. It could do anything a horse could do except at-
tract flies. Plowing, planting, and cultivating could be
done in one third the time and without blisters or back-
ache. A way to reduce physical labor was always fore-
most in Henry's mind.

With the automobile on the farms, the tractor became
a necessity. The farmer had been introduced to power.
He did not need new tools so much as power to run the
tools he had.

Henry followed exactly the same course in building
his tractor as he did with the automobile. Each part of
the tractor had to be as strong as was possible to make it.
The parts were few in number. The automobile was de-

signed to carry. The tractor was designed to pull and climb. That difference in function made all the difference in the world in construction. Henry's hardest problem was to get bearings that would stand up against the heavy pull. His finished product was a four cylinder engine that started by gasoline but ran with kerosene. The lightest weight he could attain with strength was 2,425 pounds. The grip was in the lugs on the driving wheels, as in the claws of a cat.

In addition to its pulling jobs, the tractor was designed for work as a stationary engine. When it was not at work in the fields, it could be hitched up with a belt to run machinery. Besides plowing, harrowing, cultivating and reaping, it could thresh, run grist mills and various other sorts of mills, pull stumps, and plow snow.

During the First World War the government made a test of a Fordson to see how its costs compared with doing the work with horses:

Cost, Fordson, $880. Wearing life 4,800 hours at 4/5 acre per hour, 3,840 acres.

3,840 acres at $880; depreciation per acre	.221
Repairs for 3,840 acres, $100; per acre	.026
Fuel cost, kerosene at 19 cents; 2 gal. per acre	.38
Driver $2 per day, 8 acres; per acre	.25
¾ gal. oil per 8 acres; per acre	.075
Cost of plowing with Fordson; per acre	.95

8 Horses cost, $1,200. Working Life 5,000 hours at 4/5 acre per hour, 4,000 acres

4,000 acres at $1,200; depreciation of horses per acre	.30
Feed per horse, 40 cents (100 working days) per acre	.40
Feed per horse, 10 cents a day (265 idle days) per acre	.265
Two drivers two gang plows, at $2 each per day, per acre	.50
Cost of plowing with horse; per acre	1.46

Power farming was the new way to farm, and it was cheaper. "Work cannot be removed from any life that is productive," Henry told reporters when he was interviewed about the tractor, "but power farming does mean that drudgery can be removed from the farm. It takes the burden from flesh and blood and puts it on steel."

The new house was completed and named "Fairlane." It was furnished with massive furniture in keeping with the large structure. A gate-man was stationed at the entrance and no one could enter the grounds without previous arrangements. In Detroit the Fords were constantly annoyed by people wanting money and favors. There were appeals for charity, for jobs, for financial support or approval of gadgets of invention. Now Clara and Henry could have a private home life without strangers pouncing upon them.

At about the same time Henry began to build a similiar defensive barrier at his factories and private offices. It was harder to see him than the President of the United States. Requests for interviews had to go through numerous hands. Only if the requests impressed the subordinates did Henry learn about them.

Neither Clara nor Henry had a desire for extravagant luxury or display. They did enjoy entertaining a few old friends most informally. They both loved their spacious grounds. Henry liked to walk across country and jump fences. He placed five hundred birdhouses throughout the many acres and called them his "bird hotels." The Hotel Pontchartrain was a huge martin house with seventy-six apartments. The wrens, Henry knew, liked swaying nests. For them he mounted a number of wren boxes on strips of spring steel so they would sway in the wind.

All winter long he kept wire baskets of food hanging about on the trees. And a big basin of water was kept from freezing by an electric heater. In the summer he ordered cherries left on the trees and strawberries open in beds.

One evening Henry came home and handed Clara a magazine. "I want you to read this article," Henry said, the corners of his mouth twitching with amusement.

"Why, it's by John Burroughs, the famous naturalist writer," Clara exclaimed, as she glanced at the page.

"He's got a grudge against modern progress," Henry explained. "He dislikes the noise of factories and railways. He criticizes industrial progress because it gives people money and power to despoil the lovely countryside. He declares the automobile is going to kill the appreciation of nature."

"Why, of all things," Clara fumed, "someone should set him straight on how the automobile will promote the appreciation of nature!"

"I did," Henry chuckled, tossing a letter to Clara. "The article came out months ago. When I read it, I sent Mr. Burroughs a Ford with the request that he try it and discover for himself whether it would not help him to know nature better. The letter came today. He says it took him some time to learn how to manage the automobile himself, but it has completely changed his point of view. He finds that it helps him to see more, and from now on he will make most of his bird-hunting expeditions behind the steering wheel."

"Now, isn't that a marvelous accomplishment for an old gentleman. Why don't you invite him to visit us?" Clara suggested. She knew how much Henry enjoyed Mr. Burroughs' books.

"That's a wonderful idea," Henry agreed enthusiastically.

John Burroughs did visit the Fords and a fine friendship grew between the two men. Mr. Burroughs thought Henry not only had more but more varied kinds of bird callers than anywhere else in the northern states.

When Mr. Burroughs told Henry he had changed his views on industry, Henry was more than a little pleased because he knew he had had something to do with changing them. "Henry," Mr. Burroughs said, "I've come to see that the whole world could not live by hunting birds' nests."

During one of their conversations, Henry said, "You

know, John, the only time I ever used the Ford organization to influence legislation was on behalf of the birds, and I think the end justified the means."

Mr. Burroughs, who looked like a small Santa Claus, smiled under his white beard.

"The Weeks-McLean Bird Bill," Henry explained, "which provided for bird sanctuaries for our migratory birds, was hanging in Congress with every likelihood of dying a natural death. Its immediate sponsors could not arouse much interest among the Congressmen." Henry thumped the table with his fist indignantly because the bill had received no interest. "Birds do not vote!" he added sarcastically.

Mr. Burroughs snickered at Henry's wrath. He was not always pleased with politics either.

"Well," Henry went on, "we got behind that bill and we asked each of our six thousand agents to wire to his representative in Congress. It began to become apparent that birds might have votes. The bill went through!"

Before Mr. Burroughs died in 1921, Henry and he went on several camping trips with Thomas Edison and Harvey Firestone, the tire manufacturer. They did their own cooking and lived very ruggedly. These vagabond trips were made in motor caravans and they slept under canvas. The trips were good fun. Once they gypsied through the Adirondacks and another time through the Alleghenies, heading southward.

The camping excursions were an opportunity for Burroughs, Edison, and Firestone to relax, but not Henry. A rippling stream was an invitation for Henry to race up and down the bank, measuring the fall of water and figuring out its energy if it were harnessed. Then he

would talk about the benefit that would come to every country neighborhood if the water power going to waste in its valley streams were set to work in some useful industry, furnishing employment to the farmers and others in the winter seasons. He was always thinking of the greatest benefits to the greatest number.

Mr. Burroughs said, "No poet ever expressed himself through his work more completely than Henry has expressed himself through his car and his tractor engine. They typify him — not imposing nor complex. Henry is a national figure, and the crowds that flock around the car in which he is riding are not paying their homage merely to a successful car builder or business man, but to a beneficent force."

If Henry were not inspecting the nearest stream, he would be rustling wood for a fire. His mind and body worked for play.

CHAPTER 21

ORE AND MORE buildings went up on the River
Rouge site. The stockholders opposed investing
the surplus profits of the company in such a stupenduous
plant. They wanted the money to come to them in
dividends. Henry didn't listen to them and went ahead
with his plans. Then the stockholders got a court order
for Henry to turn over more profits to them.

Henry would not have stockholders tell him how to
run his business and interfere with his plans. He knew
there was only one thing for him to do — the same thing
he had done with Malcolmson.

Edsel, Henry's son, was now twenty-six years old and
an important part of the company. In 1916 he had
married Eleanor Clay, the attractive niece of J. L. Hudson,
the department store magnate of Detroit. Henry decided
that Edsel should buy the stock from the troublesome
stockholders and become president of the company.

The small group of stockholders knew Henry well enough to realize that he got what he wanted. If they refused to sell, they knew he would start another factory and make still better and cheaper automobiles.

Sixteen years before, Miss Couzens, sister to James, bought one share of stock at $100. She was paid $260,000 for that one share of stock. James Couzens sold his stock for $30,000,000. The Dodge brothers sold their $10,000 interest for $25,000,000. Other stockholders sold for a total of $62,500,000.

Now that Henry and Edsel were in complete control, Henry reincorporated the company for $100,000,000. He was ready to carry out the biggest ideas any man ever had about industry. The Rouge plant would take raw materials in on one side, and finished cars, trucks and tractors would pour out under their own power on the other side.

Every process of manufacture would be under Henry's control. He would own his own ships and railroad. He would own his supplies of raw materials, such as coal, timber, ore, and so on.

By doing this Henry thought he could eliminate waste, reduce loss of time, and the expense of manufacturing. For example, a bolt originally purchased from the Western Automatic Screw Machine Company at $50 a thousand Henry found could be manufactured by him at a cost of $8.70 a thousand. He saved $582,635 on that bolt alone during its first year of manufacture in his own plant. These savings, he believed, could be passed on to car purchasers in the form of reduced prices. All this had been in Henry's mind when he bought the swamp ground back in 1915.

Henry's eagle-eyes watched the work progress at the Rouge. Dredges were widening and deepening the river. On a bright, sunny day a dredge swung around and dumped its contents a few feet from where he was standing. "Stop that dredge," Henry shouted. A muskrat was trapped in the pile of mud and was struggling to free itself. The workmen hurried to help the animal. "No," Henry ordered, "leave it alone. It can take care of itself."

The dredge stood still for an hour. Everyone waited for the muskrat to regain its strength in the warm sunlight. Finally, it labored to its feet and, slowly, disappeared under the bank.

Henry raised his hand and signalled the workers to continue.

The new power plant at the Rouge was one of Henry's chief interests. He was still a lover of steam engines and wanted to use them whenever he could. However, he kept his finger on power progress. He had read a great deal about the work of Sir Charles Algernon Parsons, a British engineer, who was the inventor of the steam turbine which revolutionized marine travel. His famous *Turbiana*, the first vessel to be propelled by turbines, was completed in 1897. The amazing speed immediately claimed the attention of the world.

Henry knew that a reciprocating steam engine, one which has a piston working forward and backward, would require about forty pounds of steam per horsepower where a modern turbine would average about eight pounds per horsepower. It was more economical to use turbines.

Four boilers and two giant turbo-electric generator units were installed to supply steam and electric power to the plant. Later, a third giant turbo-electric generator unit was added. The boilers operated at 250 pounds 625 degrees Fahrenheit, with a steaming capacity of 200,000 pounds per hour each. The two 12,500 KW units were of General Electric design, operating at 250 pounds and exhausting against a back pressure of one pound absolute. The electric load at this time was easily carried by one of the two units. The turbo generators, including condensers, were about as high as a two story house. The steam shooting against the blades forced the blades around as air forces a windmill to turn. Engineers all over the country watched with interest the performance of these boilers, for they were the first large units to burn coal in the pulverized form, which is finer than talcum powder.

Water used for cooling and manufacturing purposes was obtained from the Rouge River. But it was soon discovered that the Rouge River was not satisfactory. At certain periods of the year there was scarcely any flow. Water temperature ran as high as 87 degrees Fahrenheit at times with a year around average temperature of 65 degrees Fahrenheit.

As the Rouge plant expanded, more, cleaner, and cooler water was needed. Since this cool water could not be obtained from the Rouge River, Henry's engineers solved this problem by building an underground tunnel running between the Detroit River and the Rouge plant. This tunnel was 12,000 feet long with a capacity of 913,000,000 gallons per twenty-four hours.

Henry's glass factory made better glass cheaper than he could buy it. He bought forests to supply wood. He mined his coal in his own Kentucky mines. The iron came from his own land in his own steamships.

He bought a railroad with 105 miles of track. Loco-motives were still a wondrous sight to Henry. He would always marvel at the power of steam that moved them. But he bought the D. T. & I., or the Detroit, Toledo & Ironton Railroad to meet his needs to build Fords. For more than thirty years the railroad had been owned by many companies without profit. Henry's purchase of the railroad was not for the profit he might have made from it, but for the huge saving its operation would bring to his manufacturing enterprise on the Rouge River.

Like everything else under Henry's control the eight-een locomotives of the D. T. & I. were kept shining clean and the bright work sparkled.

Even crossing watchmen played an important role in creating a small model railroad. They kept the crossings clean and performed work without sending for section-men. Instead of receiving the former scale of $58 a month, they received $156. Such jobs were eagerly sought and jealously guarded. The salaries of all the railway employees were increased accordingly.

The line was provided with new ballast. Ties, rails and other materials of heavier weight were installed. Henry improved ditching, rebuilt locomotives, widened banks, cleared the right of way and removed unsightly and old buildings. The dinky little old railroad that nobody could make money on did a big job for Henry and did it well. It served the "Machine Shop of the World" with clock-like precision.

When the first of the two giant blast furnaces in the new plant was completed, Henry planned a christening for it. It was to be called Henry II, in honor of his first grandson. To make the christening complete, Henry decided the baby should attend the ceremony.

"Henry," Clara scolded, "you're not going to take that baby down to the factory! Land sakes alive, the firing of a blast furnace is no place for our two-year-old grandson."

"Now, Clara, nothing will hurt him," Henry insisted, "and besides he's got to learn about these things sometime. Why, hang it all, he's going to be the next president of the Ford Motor Company."

"Nonsense," Clara sputtered, knowing she was defeated, "I wouldn't blame Eleanor if she didn't allow you to take the baby."

The chubby, dark curly-headed Henry II attended the christening wide-eyed with the excitement but with nary a thought that he was witnessing the starting point of steel production at the Rouge, or that he would someday be the president of the gigantic enterprise.

Clara kept close watch on the baby in spite of the fact that he was in his grandfather's arms most of the time. And she was greatly relieved when he was safely returned to the Grosse Pointe estate, where Edsel and Eleanor lived.

CHAPTER 22

T HE WORLD WAS changing rapidly. Rural concrete
roads, less than five miles at the beginning of the
Model T's career, increased to 31,000 miles. News of the
world was beginning to be given out by radio broad-
casters, and folks clamped earphones on their heads to
listen.

Henry was sixty years old in 1923, but he was ready to
challenge more colossal tasks. In 1922 he had taken over
the Lincoln Motor Company. The fine Lincoln car was
high-priced and universally respected. Henry's sales-
manship talents were still devoted to the "universal car"
but the Lincoln was the answer to the critics who poked
fun at the Model T.

On a 306 acre site, in London, Henry had built the
Dagenham plant. It was the second largest in the world
and next in size to the River Rouge plant. With a front-

age on the Thames the plant had facilities for water, rail, and motor transport. The Dagenham plant manufactured, assembled and distributed cars for markets of Great Britain, Ireland and some of the British possessions.

South American branches were linked directly with Dearborn and the Rouge, while in Germany, France, Holland, and Belgium the same policy was followed as in Great Britain. Part of the stock in these countries was held by its citizens.

Henry turned to a rubber development project and leased more than four million acres of jungle in Brazil. Nothing seemed too much for him to undertake. "The bigger a business is, the easier it is to run," Henry said.

His interests by this time led to outside activities which had no more direct bearing on motor-making than any other business, but which he regarded as beneficial to human progress.

He built the Ford Hospital in Detroit, and announced that it would be for anyone needing medical care. Resident doctors would not practice outside, and patients would have examinations by a sufficient number of physicians to insure a correct diagnosis. Millions of dollars went to work without a profit.

Many more millions went into educational work. Henry was always interested in young people and children. He did many things to help them get knowledge and learn how to get along in the world. He founded the Henry Ford Trade School. This school was to help boys prepare themselves for positions in industry. The boys spent their time in the school classrooms and in the school shops.

In the fall of 1923 Henry and Dr. Hugo Eckner, the German "lighter-than-air" student, stood on the ground of Henry's partially completed airport. Dr. Eckner had just delivered the dirigible ZR-3 to the United States government. The two men were discussing the possibilities of large, rigid type airships.

"The next time you come to Detroit you should bring your airship with you," Henry said.

Dr. Eckner shook his head regretfully. "I'd like to," he replied, "but you have here no mooring mast."

Henry smiled. "That's easy. I'll build one," he said. Nothing was impossible for Henry.

The following spring Henry built a $500,000 mooring mast for dirigibles to accommodate any airship up to 10,000,000 cubic feet capacity. The Shenandoah, the American-made dirigible, was to have been its first guest, but en route to Detroit it crashed in Ohio during a storm and many lives were lost.

The ZR-3 did visit the Ford Airport in 1926, on the second anniversary of its cross-Atlantic flight. It was re-named the Los Angeles by the U.S. Navy.

The Navy built two super dirigibles, the Akron and Macon, but both came to grief through structural failure. As a result, the Ford mooring mast, which might other-wise have served as an important mid-western mooring for Naval lighter-than-air craft, did not get much use. But Henry stood ready and willing to assist aviation in all its phases.

Early in 1924 Henry and Edsel became interested in the efforts of a Detroit aeronautical engineer, William B. Stout, to organize a company for the express purpose of building an all-metal Liberty-engined cargo and passen-

ger plane. "We are working on our airport in Dearborn. There will be a hangar and a factory," Henry said to Stout. "You may use them if you wish."

Following completion of the factory, the Stout Metal Airplane Company moved in and was renamed the Stout Airplane Division of the Ford Motor Company. It was that year that the first Ford tri-motor was completed. This was a plane that pilots regarded very highly.

This airplane was far ahead of all contemporary design. Whereas commercial airplanes up to this time were makeshift conversions of wood and fabric military models, costly to operate and low on performance, the Ford tri-motor was of all-metal construction and sturdily built. Equipped as a passenger carrier, it had room for eight passengers or a ton of freight. Top speed was 116; cruising speed, 100; landing speed, 55 miles an hour.

The arrival of the Ford tri-motor was timely, for transport aviation had by the mid-twenties reached the toddling age, and a comfortable, dependable and economical airplane capable of carrying a substantial payload was needed.

The Ford tri-motor was not the first large, all-metal air transport built. Dr. Junkers experimented with metal construction in Germany at about the same time. But

FIRST FORD-STOUT AIRPLANE, THE 'MAIDEN DEARBORN I' (NOT THE FLIVVER PLANE.) TRI-MOTOR OPPOSITE.
1925

the tri-motor was the first practical all-metal design to reach the production stage.

The big silver ship was called "the tin-goose" by pilots everywhere. When Commander Richard E. Byrd flew from Little America on the edge of the Antarctic over the South Pole and back, his plane was a Ford tri-motor.

Byrd left the ship at the pole for a year, and upon his return found the big ship completely encased in ice. It was dug free, the carburetor cleaned, batteries installed, and started without difficulty.

Henry, whose interest in engines extended to all phases of transportation, thought the coming thing would be an inexpensive and safe, light airplane suitable for the average citizen. He gave orders to two of his engineers to design an experimental single passenger flivver plane. His only specific directions were: "Make it safe, inexpensive, and reliable."

It was on Henry's birthday in 1926 that the first Ford flivver took to the air smoothly and gracefully at Ford Airport. A tiny, low-winged monoplane of a semi-cantilever construction, with a wing span of 25 feet and a fuselage 16 feet 6 inches long, soared into the sky, proud of its 5 feet height and 550 pound weight.

The first model was powered by a 45 horsepower

Anzani three-cylinder radial engine of French manufacture. Harry Brooks, the pilot, flew the tiny ship from his home in Birmingham to the Ford Airport each day. He astonished his neighbors by taking off and landing on a small vacant field, roadways and even sidewalks. The ship was stable and easy to control, and it carried its single occupant along at approximately 85 miles an hour.

The second model of the flivver was a two-cylinder, horizontally opposed aircooled engine replacing the Anzani. Instead of carrying twelve gallons of gasoline, the new model carried fifty gallons of gasoline.

One windy day in the mid-twenties, Henry watched one of his tri-motors coming in for a landing. The three engines were idling as the plane glided toward the runway, and its wings wobbled in the rough eddies sweeping across the field. Turning to a companion, Henry said, "A method must be found so that an airplane can use its power in landing. That's where many serious accidents occur. You see, when an airplane starts to land, the power is shut off and it is helpess — in the power of the elements — from that time until it stops."

Years later, Henry watched the Douglas DC-3 pilots glide to a comfortable landing with power on, and flaps extended to retard the ship's speed.

Another of Henry's advanced ideas on airplane engines in the mid-nineteen twenties was: Make it produce one horsepower for each pound and a half weight, and about 1000 horsepower will be enough for a start. An expert told him that the proposal for one horsepower per pound and a half weight was most radical, but nothing in Henry's career had taught him to believe a thing impossible.

Eight years later the engines that lifted off the Dearborn airport developed 1,000 horsepower each. And they produced one horsepower for each 1.07 pounds of weight. Henry's ideas were always several years ahead of actual progress.

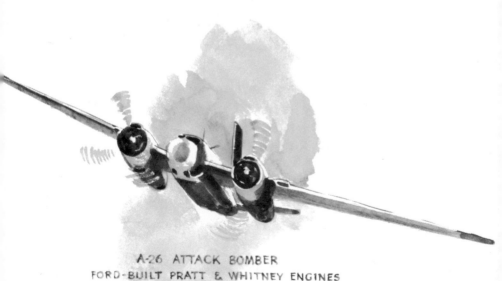

A-26 ATTACK BOMBER
FORD-BUILT PRATT & WHITNEY ENGINES
2000 H.P.
1945

CHAPTER 23

IT WAS IN 1925 that Henry's company reached the record production of 10,000 Model T cars in one day. He was selling 41 percent of the cars produced in America. In 1927 he turned out his 15 millionth Model T.

He had proved to the world that manufacturers could raise wages, cut prices, produce in tremendous volume, and still make millions. He taught the world to produce an abundance of goods with the minimum of human effort and toil. He taught the world that industrial production could give workers increased purchasing power to buy industrial products and live on a higher standard — that was the meaning of his revolutionary $5 a day minimum wage. But according to Henry's principle, this was only possible if the worker were willing to give a good day's work for his wage. A man or woman who did not earn his salary could not hold his job with the Ford Motor Company.

After experimenting with the five-day week for a year, Henry reached the conclusion that the shorter period of labor increased production in his plants. Not less work, but better and more work in less time, with better methods and better tools, was the Ford policy.

For nineteen years the little, rattling Model T had given the poor man of America reliable independent transportation. Each year they had been as alike as two peas in a pod. The purchaser could have any color he wanted as long as it was black.

But the time had arrived when refinements in automobile construction were regarded as necessities. As the scale of living rose, it was logical that comfort in transportation must keep pace with the ever increasing comforts of living generally. The American people changed their idea of what an inexpensive car should be like. They wanted something flashier with more style. The Chevrolet, in the same price bracket, could give them what they wanted. It had advanced appearance, power and comfort. Buyers turned to this car. Chevrolet took the lead in sales that Henry's Model T had held for so many years.

Henry was dead set on the idea that a utility car did not need to have style and comfort. Edsel was not a chip off the old block. He would often disagree with his father. Henry would listen to Edsel's arguments but if he had already made up his mind, nothing could change it.

"Dad," Edsel insisted, "we've got to dress up the Ford. The Model T will have to be scrapped so we can do something about the competition Chevrolet is giving us!"

"That's just a fad," Henry scoffed. "They'll come back to the utility car."

Henry's successful production of fifteen million Model T cars made him the richest and most famous individual in automobile history. He convinced the public that the automobile was good. But when the public was convinced that the automobile was good, buyers wanted cars to be good looking and comfortable too. People no longer wanted automobiles that were as alike as pins or matches. The homely black Model T had outlived its welcome in the hearts of Americans.

When sales and profits dwindled and dwindled, Henry was forced to follow Edsel's ideas.

Henry, Edsel, and the engineers worked hard on the new model that was to compete with Chevrolet in 1927. Henry spent $100,000,000, scrapped thirty thousand tools and started all over again, following the lead of General Motors in a trend of automobile designing for comfort and style in the low-priced field. It wasn't easy for Henry to build these ideas into a model, because he did not believe beauty was necessary in an inexpensive car.

The new styled car meant making the plants over completely for production. Plans were kept very secret. None

of the new features or details were given to the public.

In 1927 the Model A was introduced in Ford show-rooms all over the country. Ford dealers were happy to have something with dash to compete with the Chevrolet dealers. The new model was very different from the Model T. The day of the "Tin Lizzie" was gone forever. Newspapers published cartoons dramatizing the death of "Lizzie." She had been a rattlin' good car in her day.

Refinements galore adorned the Model A. There were a variety of colors instead of black. It had more speed, four-wheel brakes, standard gearshift, safety glass, longer wheel base, a lower hung chassis, and shock absorbers. What the public liked most of all was the announcement of the cost of the new Ford. It was practically the same as the old Model T.

Henry advertised the new Model A as a new car from radiator cap to rear axle. He advertised the 40 horse-power engine that would do 55 and 60 miles an hour, and its mechanical, four-wheel brakes.

The oiling system was specially designed by Henry's engineers. It was a combination of pump, splash, and gravity feed. The pump delivered the oil to the valve chamber, from which it flowed by gravity feed to the main bearings of the crankshaft. An oil dipper was pro-vided on each connecting-rod bearing cap, so that the force of rotation of the crankshaft drove oil into the connecting-rod bearings, as well as splashing oil over all parts within the engine.

Henry still clung to the policy that it is better to sell a large number of cars at a small margin of profit than to sell a few cars at a large margin of profit. But he knew, too, that only if the design is good for years and years can mass production be the cheapest way to give the product to the world. To produce two gears in the new rear axle, 43,000 machine tools had to be altered, and 4,500 brand new ones built. The dies which replaced the old ones alone cost $5,000,000.

Henry hoped the Model A would repeat the history of the Model T with a long successful life. It didn't. Many people thought it couldn't hold a candle to the Chevrolet. Chevrolet was advancing fast and giving the people up-to-the-minute styling. Model A lived only five years.

JRT

CHAPTER 24

IT WAS A beautiful day in May 1927. "Clara," Henry
called as he entered the wide hall filled with flowers,
pleasant paintings, and dark, shining furniture. There
was no answer. He wandered out to the sun porch, a
wide room whose whole height was framed in glass.

Clara was doing a piece of needle point and listening
to the radio. Henry smiled as he watched her intent upon
her handwork and the program. He was glad she was
home. Home just wasn't home without Clara. If she
happened to be out when Henry came home, he was restless until she returned.

Riches had come to Clara, but like Henry, her wants
and needs still were simple. She looked much younger
than her years. She was wearing a dark blue crepe de
Chine dress, black stockings, and conservatively cut black
oxfords. Her glasses hung on a piece of black ribbon —

no chain of gold, platinum, nor diamonds. Her eyes were dark and alert with a lilt of brightness in them, and steady and clear like Henry's.

"I didn't hear you come in, dear," Clara said in surprise, as she quickly got up and fluffed a pillow in Henry's chair to make him comfortable. "You'll want to hear this program. That young Lindbergh boy has just arrived in Paris in his 'Spirit of St. Louis.' He's an overnight hero of this generation."

"A great accomplishment — a young fellow twenty-five years old, covering a nonstop flight of 3,610 miles in thirty-three and a half hours in a monoplane!" Henry marvelled. "I'll bet my bottom dollar that boy has an ear for engines that is as sensitive as a doctor's stethoscope. He should do a big service for science during his lifetime."

"The people are surely taking him to their hearts. Just listen to the welcome he is receiving in France," Clara said. Like thousands of other Americans, Clara and Henry were sharing Charles Lindbergh's great moment with him.

When the program was over, Clara watched Henry writing on some scraps of paper he pulled out of his pocket. "Figuring or designing — what is it now?" she asked.

"Just figuring what we spent for mechanical devices when we were married."

"My goodness, Henry, that was thirty-odd years ago. Why bother about that?"

"Thought it might be interesting to compare our list with the mechanical devices available to young married people today."

"Humph, no doubt our list sounds as if we were pioneers."

"We did have a few things the pioneers couldn't boast about. We bought:

2 bicycles	$70
Wringer and washboard	5
Sewing machine	25
Brushes and brooms	5
Total	$105

"Nowadays a young couple needs quite a tidy sum if they want to own all the mechanical devices of the mechanical age:

Automobile, a Ford, of course	$700
Radio	75
Phonograph	50
Washing machine	150
Electric refrigerator	250
Vacuum cleaner	50
Electric sewing machine	60
Oil heater	500
Toaster, electric iron, etc	25
Telephone, per year	35
Total	$1895

"Times have certainly changed since the 'horse and buggy' days when we were married." Henry cocked his head with satisfaction, approving the progress of the world.

"Those things are fine to have," Clara said, "they save labor, provide pleasure, and make a better world to live in, but not many young people have that much money. We couldn't have afforded all those things, even if they had been available."

"Maybe I wouldn't have been able to buy them for you the first year we were married, but I'd have had them before long. It's about time people wake up and realize that prosperity and happiness can come only through honest effort."

"Henry," Clara said thoughtfully, "one day I heard you tell one of your friends, 'As we serve our jobs we serve the world,' what did you mean?"

"Why, it's as plain as the nose on your face, Clara. I have no patience with the fellow who works just for money and doesn't care an iota how he does his job. Every so often we run across a fellow who thinks the world owes him a living, instead of him owing the world a good day's work. Those fellows don't care a hang how they do their work — all they care about is the money they get for putting in their time on the job."

Henry crossed his legs and locked his hands about his knees, which was a characteristic position when he was trying to put his thoughts into words. "Money will come naturally as the result of service," he said. "It is absolutely necessary to have money, but we don't want to forget that the end of money is not ease but the opportunity to perform more service. Life is like pulling your weight in a boat. Many a man wants to be a passenger, but pulling his weight blisters his hands."

Clara could no more imagine Henry sitting around twiddling his thumbs than she could think of herself doing a ballet dance. She wished everyone might know how sincere and genuine were Henry's interests. She knew that when Henry worked with his first engine he did not think in terms of making money or of getting rich, but of mastering the principle of a gasoline engine. His ideas now were to build many factories, many cars, and provide work for many people. His interests always were for the good of many people.

"By the way," Clara said, after all these thoughts had swirled through her mind, "how is your educational project coming?"

Henry had set aside two hundred acres at Dearborn to reproduce American life through the ages. This project was called The Edison Institute and Greenfield Village. Henry believed that by looking at things people used and showing the way they lived in the past, a better knowledge of our history and progress could be gained. The Museum was being built to endure for generations as an exhibit of progress in engineering, mechanics, and useful arts and crafts. Henry's idea was to make the Museum and Village become one of the historic spots of the world.

"Fine, fine," Henry said enthusiastically, "I've got scouts all over and they are sending in hundreds of articles and appliances of the old days. Each article that comes in is restored to its usable state. And when I see old engines and machines work again, I'm as tickled as a boy with a new whistle!"

"I suspect," Clara smiled, "that you are spending most of your time with the exhibit of engineering and mechanics."

"Sometimes I watch an old engine run for thirty or forty minutes, and often I get some new idea our engineers can work out for the Ford car."

While most men Henry's age were retiring or slowing up and taking life a bit easier, Henry had a hundred irons in the fire, and he worked from early morning until late at night to make the world a better place to live in.

CHAPTER 25

PEOPLE FROM ALL OVER the world came to visit the famous Edison Institute and Greenfield Village. This enduring monument to remind people of their country's past was, in its way, a service as valuable as Henry's contribution of the "universal car." Sightseers who came in search of knowledge found that they were being delightfully entertained. Those who came out of mere curiosity or for diversion found that they were being educated in spite of themselves.

From an engine of 1760 a visitor could trace the history of steam power through every phase of the machine age. The exhibit showed that with the coming of power, the whole method of manufacturing and living conditions had been completely changed. The story of steam power started with the beginning of the first commercial English steam engines, the Newcomen atmospheric pressured engine. Then Watt's pumping engine, built in 1795, improved upon the Newcomen design by enclosing the upper end of the cylinder and using a separate condensing chamber. This prevented the cyclic cooling of the working cylinder by the condensing water stream, making considerable reduction in steam consumption.

From 1780 the crank method of producing rotative motion from reciprocating motion could be seen. These engines were used in England to draw up coal from the mines. They developed about nineteen horsepower.

Watt's 1812 "straight-line linkage" for the piston rod was of interest because it showed the first attempt to admit steam at both ends of the cylinder alternately, thereby greatly increasing the development of power in a given space and size of machine.

In the American steam engine group, visitors saw the development in marine steam engines beginning with a two-cylinder, horizontal, simple and crude type that was used in river boats in the South for nearly one hundred years. The connecting rods were often of wood, sometimes iron-bound, and were connected directly to the shaft of the stern paddle wheel.

Another section of American steam engine development showed advancement of slide valve designs, releasing valve gears, automatic governors, and high-speed engines.

Students could observe the differences between the English and American engines. The English engines were given great attention by the manufacturers in quality of finish, with fancy ironwork and railings that were generally furnished as part of the engine installation. The American manufacturer built for utility primarily, with very little decoration and railings.

It gave Henry great satisfaction to know he was making it possible for boys who liked engines to see the world's greatest collection in Dearborn.

The collections of the Museum were divided into five principal groups: fine arts, agriculture, household arts, manufacturing and power, and transportation. Each group was just as extensive as the steam engine group.

Greenfield Village was really another museum with many small buildings gathered around an old-fashioned greensward. No automobiles were allowed in the village, and horses and carriages carried visitors from building to building. An atmosphere of seventy-five years ago had been restored.

In a rectangular yard with a white picket fence around it stood the Menlo Park group of buildings which were reconstructed from or reproductions of the structure in which Thomas A. Edison labored from 1876 to 1886. The early models of the incandescent light, the first phonograph, the original carbon telephone transmitter, and the first mimeograph were all demonstrated.

There were many historic restorations that had a sentimental interest for Henry: the original Ford homestead, where Henry was born; his small brick workshop as it stood at 58 Bagley Avenue, Detroit, where he built his

first gasoline vehicle; the old red Scottish Settlement schoolhouse, where he emptied his pockets on the teacher's desk and carved his initials in his desk.

From an earlier period Henry reconstructed the log cabin, which was the birthplace of William Holmes McGuffey, one of the great educators of America, whose readers were used by Henry and thousands of other boys and girls throughout the land.

The cottage birthplace of Stephen Collins Foster, one of Henry's favorite composers, was moved from Pennsylvania. And the Lincoln courthouse, a two-story walnut structure, was brought from Logan County, Illinois. Countless other historical buildings were moved to Dearborn.

Henry did not always move historical places to Dearborn. In some cases he bought and renovated old buildings and left them at their original sites. The Wayside Inn, at South Sudbury, Massachusetts, is one of these.

"Learning by doing," was one of Henry's basic beliefs. It was a theory he learned early in his workshop on the farm. It was with this idea in mind that he started the first Greenfield Village School with thirty children present. This system of schools grew until it extended from kindergarten through an accredited high school.

To train each child to find a place for himself in the world was another of the school's objectives. One day of each school week was spent in "learning to do by doing" in the high school. Students chose jobs which they thought would best teach them attitudes and skills of value in their life work. Jobs ranged from assisting the Village teachers to technical work in radio. Some of the girls performed the routine tasks of a large business office, and some of the boys worked as apprentice machinists.

In all jobs the students worked side by side with the regular employees.

Scarcely a day passed that Henry did not attend chapel service with the students in the Martha-Mary Chapel. Often he gave the students a few of his thoughts. One day he talked about faith. He explained how boys and girls could acquire faith.

"Begin with faith in anything you can believe in, and you'll be surprised how far it will take you," Henry said. "If you begin with belief in yourself, you get confidence in other men. If you have confidence in other men, you gain faith in your country, and finally you reach the conviction that somewhere there is a Law of Right which makes things go right. And when you reach that the whole wide range is open to you. . . .

"I believe that faith works. If a man starts doing something he believes in, and does it with a motive which the universe can respect — that is, to make life more liveable for others as well as himself — his belief in his work will draw to him the means to do that work. . . .

"One of the greatest discoveries a man makes, one of his greatest surprises, is to find he *can* do what he was afraid he couldn't do. . . . "

One snowy winter's day Henry and Edsel brought Mr. Edgar Guest, the poet, to the Chapel to talk to the children. Mr. Guest recited many of his poems. One the children enjoyed particularly was: "When Father Shook the Stove." Henry and Edsel sat in the back of the Chapel and enjoyed the beaming faces of the students as much as they did Mr. Guest. Often Henry brought famous and interesting speakers for this service. They ranged from baseball players to noted scientists.

There were beautiful, old-fashioned dancing parties for the boys and girls at Lovett Hall, which is undoubtedly one of the most gorgeous ballrooms in the country. The teakwood floor came all the way from East India. The exquisite, sparkling, crystal chandeliers draw everyone's admiration. They are a cut glass with a large percentage of lead, and were made in Czechoslovakia. The furniture is of eighteenth century design and the china in the cabinets scattered throughout the room was taken from the choice Museum collection.

The ballroom is used each week for Early American Dancing lessons for grade and high school students. When a real dancing party was held, Clara and Henry would attend too. During the evening Henry would dance with Clara, the teachers, and some of the older girls. These party gatherings not only enabled the students to learn the old-fashioned dances but they learned courtesy and poise.

Henry expressed his aims in building the Museum and Greenfield Village when he said, "When we are through, we shall have reproduced American life as lived; and that, I think, is the best way of preserving at least a part of our history and tradition."

CHAPTER 26

ONE MORNING HENRY stopped at the Armington &
Sims Machine Shop, which was one of the early
shops in the East that Henry moved to Greenfield Village.
In the shop, with its many machines, was one of the first
with a shaft governor and center crank construction. This
was one of the most successful in driving the early electric generators, and much favored by Thomas Edison.

A young boy was absorbed in this particular shining
steam engine. He wore a pork-pie hat with a feather
stuck in the side.

"Did you shoot a bird to get that feather?" Henry
asked. He was always concerned about the conservation
of birds.

The boy was startled as he recognized the great man
that stood beside him. "No, sir," he said honestly, "the
only things I ever shoot are frogs, down at Roulo Creek."

Henry laughed heartily. "I used to do that myself when I was a boy. What's your name, son?"

"Albert Sanderson, sir."

"Guess I don't know any of your kinfolk. You interested in steam engines, Albert?"

"I sure like to watch them run!"

"Come along with me and I'll show you a dandy over at the Soy Bean Laboratory. See this suit I have on? It's made of soybean wool. Great possibilities in the use of soybeans, Albert. I'll beat you in a foot-race across the green," Henry challenged.

Albert was huffing and puffing when the race ended. "Gee, you sure can run fast, Mr. Ford," Albert panted as Henry finished several yards in the lead.

"Not bad for a man over sixty-five, eh? Running and riding a bicycle keep me healthy and spry," Henry confessed. "A man needs plenty of fresh air and exercise to keep fit."

Albert was very excited to have an important man like Mr. Ford take the time to show him around the laboratory and explain the engines. He would never forget this day.

"What's your ambition in life, son?" Henry asked.

Albert wasn't sure what he wanted to do when he grew up. But Henry never missed an opportunity to give a boy some words of guidance. "Whatever it is you want to do — do things not for money but because the work is worth-while. Do you want to be a success?" Henry asked.

"Yes, sir," Albert said emphatically.

"Then just remember these five things: cleanliness, investigation, put to use that which you already have, believe in your ability to accomplish that which you set out to do, and know how to spend money."

Albert squinted, trying to pocket all this valuable information.

Henry went on. "Once a boy has studied and investigated, we hope that he will apply his knowledge to make new combinations and produce things that will show an advance over the old. Most of our so-called new things are only new combinations of old things, like the six simple machines — wheel, pulley, lever, inclined plane, screw, and wedge — they are put together in different ways to make locomotives, automobiles, watches, and all of our complex machinery."

Albert listened intently, impressed with Henry's wisdom.

"And don't forget to spend your money, lad."

"Spend my money," Albert gasped in surprise. This was not what he heard at home. He was taught to put his money in the bank.

"Sure thing, spend your money," Henry repeated. "Spend your money for things that will put you ahead of where you were yesterday. Buy an old machine and take it apart. Learn how the wheels mesh. A dollar put into a book and a book mastered might change the whole course of your life. That same dollar put into the bank would yield you only a few pennies. Now which is better?"

For a few seconds Albert was very confused because his parents had taught him that one saved money to get ahead. "Well, I guess you ought to know, Mr. Ford," he said skeptically, "you got ahead all right."

Henry laughed and took out his watch. "By George, I have an appointment with Mr. Ingersoll, the man who makes those dollar watches — pretty good watches too. That man did a great service for his country. I had an idea like that once. I think I could have sold my watches for fifty cents." Henry said good-bye and walked briskly away, leaving Albert to think about many things.

Like all grandfathers, Henry adored his grandchildren. Edsel and his wife, Eleanor, now had four children, Henry II, Benson, Josephine, and William. Each time the children came to visit Fairlane, Henry would build them some new toy. One of the things the children liked best was a toy farm. Henry built miniature farm machinery that could be operated by a miniature steam engine. The steam engine was named "HY-BEN-JO-BILL." There was a little farmhouse that was completely furnished in every detail. The kitchen had a workable cookstove, and a sink with a pump, so the children could cook and wash dishes. Two ponies stood in the stalls of a miniature barn. The miniature tool shed was large enough for a hayrack, harrow, disc, and a spring-tooth drag. Henry went through every process of farming with the children.

He would take the children to the Rouge and they would ride in the cab of one of his locomotives that shone as bright as a dollar. The engineer let them drive the engine and blow the whistle.

Then Henry would explain that in the locomotive the

JRT

driving wheels take the place of the flywheel of the stationary steam engine, and that the amount of power developed depends upon the quantity and pressure of the steam which enters the engine. The children liked to watch the steam come up and drive the pistons back and forth.

One day Henry took the children into his library and told them a story about a new kind of engine he had been reading about. It was invented by Rudolph Diesel in 1893. The new engine would use oil and air. It would not require an electric spark or carburetor. Henry II and Benson, the two older boys, were very interested.

"Like the ordinary gas engine," Henry said, "the Diesel engine is an internal-combustion engine, because the fuel is burned in the cylinder." Henry looked at his oldest grandson, "Now, Henry, can you tell us why the steam engine is an external-combustion engine?"

Young Henry thought for a minute. "Sure, I know," he said. "The fuel is burned in a firebox separate from the cylinder where the power starts."

Henry was pleased with the answer — maybe the boy would have a mechanical mind. "When your father was a boy, he liked to build engines with me," Henry said, and waited anxiously for his oldest grandson to suggest building an engine.

"I like to sail boats and play tennis," Young Henry said decisively.

CHAPTER 27

M ODEL A LED the field in sales until October 1930, then neither the improved appearance in its variety of colors, nor its greater power and comfort could compete successfully with the smoother appearance and action of the new improved Chevrolet. General Motors had answered Henry's Model A with a flashy six-cylinder Chevrolet. The Plymouth, built by the Chrysler Corporation, was giving Henry stiff competition in the low-priced field, too.

Falling sales and Edsel's constant arguments about keeping up with current trends in automobile styling stirred Henry to action in 1931. He would go Chevrolet one better and manufacture an eight-cylinder car. "We shall continue to make the four-cylinder model. The eight is only two fours, you know," Henry told the press.

Henry, Edsel, and engineers worked for months on the

new model. Edsel thought the new model should have hydraulic brakes; the public demand was in that direction. But Henry thought mechanical brakes were safer, and what he believed, he always carried through. His opinions were as strong as the Rock of Gibraltar.

"Dad," Edsel would say, "the average automobile owner doesn't give a hoot about what goes on under the hood and under the floor, but he is interested in line and color, body design, ease of steering and riding, miles to the gallon of gas and efficiency of brakes."

"Efficiency of brakes — that's just why we won't have hydraulic brakes. You can't depend on 'em!" Henry argued staunchly.

The new model was called V-8. It cost Henry $128,447,664 over a period of two years to get into production with a new model.

The Ford Motor Company balance sheet for the six years between 1927 through 1932, and Edsel's insistence finally convinced Henry that the American public requires beauty as well as speed and dependability at low price in automobiles. Those six years revealed a total loss of $117,197,186 by the greatest and most successful automobile manufacturer. Those years covered the abandonment of Model T, the start and abandonment of the new Model A and the advance to the V-8.

The V-type engine was unique in a car selling for less than $2000. In 1914 the Cadillac had brought out the country's first eight-cylinder engine produced in quantity.

The 65-horsepower V-type engine was simple in design and construction. There were two banks of four cylinders cast in a single block integral with the crankcase.

The arrangement made possible a short, rigid crankshaft, and the entire engine required no more space than a four. The cylinders were fitted with aluminum pistons. The connecting rods and pistons were carefully matched in sets of equal weight to insure the smooth, vibrationless flow of power which the V-8 engine was capable of giving.

There was no spark lever to be operated. Henry made it automatic. A driver could shift between high and second at any speed, silently and smoothly, without clashing. The second-speed gears were of the helical cut type in constant mesh and made running in second as quiet as in high. The steering mechanism had been newly designed and handling the car became almost effortless.

There were fourteen different body styles in many colors. The new Ford sold between $460 to $650, depending upon the style. The new streamlined version seemed to have everything but hydraulic brakes, but the real test would be if the public liked it as well as Chevrolet and Plymouth.

Henry had come a long way from his ugly, black, utility Ford, but the main ideas in good automobile building were still there: simplicity of construction, unusual strength, minimum weight, use of fine materials, and accuracy in manufacture and craftsmanship — he would never sacrifice these fundamentals.

He hoped he could again command the lead in sales and put Chevrolet and Plymouth back in second and third place. But in 1932, when the V-8 was introduced, the country was in serious trouble economically and politically.

There was a great depression throughout the country and it was time for another presidential election. People blamed President Hoover for the depression. The Democratic party, led by Franklin D. Roosevelt won the election with the promise to rescue the poor workingmen who were without jobs. Even staunch Republicans turned to the Democratic ticket in the hope of helping the country out of a critical state.

The National Industrial Recovery Act, called the N.R.A., was set up with General Hugh S. Johnson as its administrator over industries, under the recovery law. Each industry had a prescribed "code." Codes were rules of action. By this means the government could regulate wages and prices.

Codification began with the larger manufacturing and production lines such as automobiles, steel, oil, textiles, railroads, lumber and ran all the way down the line to small gadgets.

The automobile industry signed a code, but Henry was not among the signers. He had always done his own thinking and was never carried by mob spirit or enthusiasm. "I'll make no public statements," he told the press. It was as if he didn't want to contest what the President thought was right, but he acted according to what he thought was right.

"How can I be opposing the President when I've insisted on high wages and shorter hours for the working man for thirty years," Henry said to Clara.

"I'm glad you have the courage to stick to what you believe is right, but I do get provoked when stupid stories
about you are spread around the country. This does give
your enemies a fine opportunity to scratch another black
mark against your name."

"Fiddlesticks," Henry scoffed, shrugging his shoulders,
"stupid stories never upset me. I can't understand why
you should mind the buzzing prattle of busybodies."

And again Henry was not bothered about public opin-
ion. After a time the N.R.A. was declared unconstitu-
tional by the Supreme Court, and Henry's competitors
were dumbfounded that Henry always managed to be on
the right side of the fence.

CHAPTER 28

"H OW TIME FLIES," Clara said to Henry one morning. "Here it is 1939, and I haven't been over to the Rouge plant in several years. I'd like to see the improvements. I have no engagements today — are you too busy to take me?"

Clara's days were now filled with board meetings for her favorite charities and garden clubs.

"Never too busy to escort my best girl. Put on your bonnet and we'll be off. By the way, the Franklin Roosevelts invited us to the White House next Thursday to meet the English king and queen, but I remembered you were having a meeting of your garden club at the house that day."

"I wouldn't think of disappointing the ladies," Clara said without further comment. Neither was any more impressed with the invitation than if they had been invited to have dinner with the mayor of Dearborn.

A chauffeur drove them to the Rouge. "Still the perfect housekeeper," Clara remarked as they drove through the grounds to the assembly lines. "Not a murky windowpane nor a heap of litter anywhere."

"My mother first taught me cleanliness and order, and then I married Clara Bryant, who is a pernickety little woman," Henry teased.

"There was one thing we both failed to teach you and that is getting to meals on time!" Clara retorted. "My, I'm glad I wore these old comfortable shoes," she said, as they started their tour. "When you told me about one hundred and thirty-two miles of conveyors, I just couldn't visualize all those moving parts."

"Here is the crankshaft and valve build up," Henry said. "As the blocks move along, the parts are put in."

"Goodness, it is interesting to watch everything move — even the valves that hang from above." Clara knew all the parts from the days she helped Henry with his first gasoline engine. She had always been an eager listener to his mechanical problems.

They walked to the piston assemblies and watched the pistons go into the motor block. More and more motor was being built with each process.

"We've gone a long way from those first days back in 1913 when we started our first moving assembly line," Henry said. "Before that we had trucks circle a building leaving parts near cars being assembled."

"Yes, and how well I remember the day they towed a chassis down a line by windlass and men put on the parts as it passed. Then came the big night when you came back from Chicago with your great idea of the assembly line — how excited you were!"

"That overhead trolley used by Chicago packers in dressing hogs gave me the idea. It was a simple mechanism by comparison with what I wanted. I knew I had to have a way for many cars to be built as rapidly as possible. And it had to be done in perfect order and at high speed with an army of workmen. But I couldn't click on the way to work out my problem until I saw those hogs jerked off their feet and hoisted, by machinery, upon a trolley ride — then my brain started working out an assembly line."

"And you not only blazed the trail for all automobile manufacturing, but for other manufacturers, too!" Clara said proudly.

"With my 'Believer' by my side," Henry affectionately patted Clara's shoulder.

After they saw the motor completed, they watched the body assembly. A steering wheel conveyor moved overhead.

"All the electric power-tools are on movable carriers too?" Clara asked.

"That's right. It takes just twenty minutes to assemble a rear axle."

"Just look," Clara exclaimed, "the motor is dropped from the conveyor above as snug as a bug in a rug."

"Now when this fender is dropped," Henry explained, "the automobile really starts to take shape."

With intense interest Clara watched the body drop from the conveyor above, then the wheels and tires were added. The car was serviced with gasoline and water and ready for tests by specialized experts.

The water test was like a combination cloudburst and tornado, shooting gigantic sprays at the rate of four hundred gallons per minute.

"Well, I must say," Clara gasped, "there couldn't be a rainstorm worse than that!"

"From here the car goes out for road tests. If these tests are satisfactory, it gets a final ticket of inspection and is loaded in the haulaway yards."

"And I'm ready to be loaded into our car — I'm exhausted. I simply can't keep up with you, Henry, you look as fresh as a daisy."

As Clara thought of all Henry's achievements, she had a very warm feeling of triumph because she knew better than anyone else the hours and hard work that had brought his ideas to the world.

Near the Rouge plant Henry was farming everything from sunflowers to soybeans. Henry was one of the first to use a new machine made by the International Harvester Company. The new machine, known as the combine, was a cross between the reaper and the threshing machine. It cut grain and separated the kernels of oats, wheat, or barley from the straw — all in one operation. Much hard labor was saved by the use of this modern harvesting machine.

Henry watched the soybeans closely. He passed the crops through his laboratory to learn how they could be used in the manufacture of automobiles and provide an industrial market for the farmer's products.

Fords were painted with a new enamel manufactured from the oil of the soybean. Freeze it, bake it or mistreat it and the original glow was not damaged. Only water was recommended as a polish because of its durability. "Keep working on this product so it will wear longer and shine better," Henry told his paint expert. He was always seeking perfection.

Soybeans could be grown in widely varying localities and rebuild rather than deplete the soil. In the laboratories the oil was extracted from the bean by dissolving it with a special gasoline solvent. A great many uses were found for the meal and the oil, such as glycerin, explosives, waterproof goods, soaps, printing ink, knobs to shift gears, horn buttons, accelerator pedals, experimental door panels and textiles.

Henry invited guests to eat a sixteen-course soybean dinner. Starting with tomato juice seasoned with soybean sauce, salted soybeans, celery stuffed with soybean cheese, purée of soybean, and soybean crackers the dinner finished with apple pie with soybean crust, soybean coffee, and soybean candy.

He made broad sweeping predictions in regard to soybeans. "We shall grow most of an automobile," he said. A Detroit Newspaper published a story: "Ford Envisions Cars Springing From the Soil."

When that story was published, the first National Farm Chemurgic Council was meeting in Dearborn. Henry went to the council with great interest. He was still searching for uses of farm products. He went too, to meet a man about whom he had heard much.

Henry's eyes searched the room. Then they rested on a rather tall, stooped Negro. He was dressed in a shabby black suit. His eyes were deep-set and gleaming like those of a dreamer with great vision.

"George Washington Carver!" Henry said, as he extended his hand. "This is a pleasure I have long looked forward to."

George Washington Carver was equally delighted to meet the industrial genius he had heard so much about.

Their eyes reflected a mutual respect and admiration.

They were about the same age, and had a great many characteristics and traits in common. They both believed in the benefit of work and work and more work! They were men who labored endless hours with no conception of time. They both believed in perseverance — if at first you don't accomplish your task, keep trying until you do. Neither man ever wasted time. Both had left the farm without money, but with a great consuming urge to satisfy a desire. Both had suffered mockery and ridicule.

That first handclasp was the beginning of a deep and warm friendship. "The great Creator gave us three kingdoms, the animal, vegetable, and mineral. Now, he has added a fourth, the synthetic," Carver said. "Tell me what you've done with the soybeans. I've read about your experiments."

The Negro listened intently as Henry told him about all the uses he had found for the meal and the oil.

"I'm going back South and use the soybeans in some of my experiments instead of peanuts," Carver said, enthusiastically.

Through that meeting Henry grew interested in the South. He bought a great tract of land near Savannah, Georgia, and transformed the poor white and Negro shacks into a successful farming acreage and experimental

station. He built two schools, calling the one for colored children, "Carver School." He built new homes and supplied farmers with equipment. Carver worked with Henry and the people, planning and showing the poor folks how to use every speck of material on the land.

Often Henry went to Tuskegee where George Washington Carver taught in the university. He would arrive in his private railway car, and they would spend hours together in Carver's room. Sometimes they would be so engrossed in their conversation they would not take time for their meals in the dining-room, and trays would be sent to them. They both liked simple foods. On fine days they often walked in the woods, talking and laughing and discussing the new things science was giving to the world.

Henry wanted to build a fine, big house for his Negro friend, but Carver shook his head and said, "A log cabin is fine enough for me."

The "Carver House" was built in Greenfield Village. Carver was delighted with his small log cabin. He spent some of his time there, working with a feverish urgency to find new uses for agricultural products.

❈❈ PART FIVE ❈❈
1941-1948

Part 5
1941~1948

CHAPTER 29

SEVERAL YEARS HAD PASSED. It was a bleak Sunday
afternoon in December 1941. Henry and Clara were
listening to the Philharmonic on the radio. Henry was
seventy-eight years old. His steps were a trifle slower, and
his hair was white instead of silver. Clara's hair was still
a soft brown, flecked with gray here and there. She wore
a smart black silk dress with a beautiful pearl necklace and
matching earrings. They were a very distinguished looking couple.

Suddenly the program was cut off. "This program is
being interrupted," the announcer stated, "to bring you
the disastrous bombing of Pearl Harbor by the Japanese."
Clara and Henry exchanged tragic glances and pulled
their chairs closer to the radio. They knew this was the
climax that would bring America into World War II.

"This will be just a rehearsal for a more terrible war

185

unless nations stop being greedy, and peoples learn how to live together in our small world," Henry told Clara.

Hating war as he did, Henry also recognized the need of production to win an early peace, and the Ford Motor Company became one of the greatest producers of war material during World War II.

Henry's first step in the war effort was to build the Willow Run Bomber Plant and adjacent flying field. He applied his principles of mass production to heavy bomber production. It was the most elaborately tooled aircraft factory in the world. The famous B-24 needed 30,000 unlike parts for a single machine. To assemble these under one roof called for the setting up of 5,450 feet of assembly lines.

The Willow Run Airport covered 1,434 acres. It served as a testing field for Willow Run Aircraft, and a training base for Army bombardment squadrons. Bombers left daily for all points of the compass.

Standing firmly for peace, as Henry did, he was bitterly criticized for his gigantic war efforts. But what would people have said about him if he had not turned his giant resources over to the government to help win the war? Henry's wealth and power had reached such great proportions that regardless of what he did, he was both

criticized and praised. But Henry cared little what people said and thought about him.

During these days when Henry was helping with the war efforts there were big problems in labor relations, too. Henry thought he was satisfying the men by giving them good salaries and good working conditions, but the labor tempests of the thirties had swept into the Ford plants. The laborer's wants had increased by leaps and bounds. The men objected to seasonal layoffs and the insecurity of their jobs. By the end of 1938 all automobile workers had been successfully organized except at Ford. Henry was still free to lower wages at will or to discharge men without rhyme or reason, if he wished.

In 1941 Henry's men voted for the CIO, which is the Congress of Industrial Organizations. This was a blow to Henry, who believed the wages he paid were always higher than any reasonable union could think of demanding and the hours of work shorter. The answer seemed to be that men wanted a way to solve their own problems in industry, just as they had a voice in running their government. Workers wanted a democracy in industry. They wanted their unions recognized.

"Labor unions are all right," Henry said, "if the official personnel were as strong, as honest, as decent, and as plainly wise as the bulk of men who make up the membership. Some of them only strive for discord — they say when you get your $12 a day, don't stop at that. Agitate for $14. When you get your eight hours a day, don't be a fool and grow contented; agitate for six hours. Start something. Always start something."

On the other hand, Henry believed unions were good for the blind bosses who never did a decent thing for their employees until they were compelled. There were bosses who cried, "Now is the time to smash labor, we've got them on the run."

The greatest victory that organized labor had won came with the passage of the Wagner Labor Relations Act in 1935. This law clearly recognized the right of workers to organize into unions. It required employers to accept collective bargaining (management and labor getting together and talking over their differences), a practice to which many employers and some workers had been opposed. To enforce this act, the National Labor Relations Board was set up.

When Henry finally agreed to a contract with the United Automobile Workers of the Congress of Industrial Organizations, UAW-CIO, in 1941, it was in many respects far more favorable to the union than that of any other automobile company. The Ford Motor Company not only agreed to a closed shop, but to the check-off, which meant only union labor would be hired and the union dues would be taken out of the worker's salary for the union to collect.

These benefits, however, did not make for the industrial peace Henry had anticipated. From 1941 to 1945 Ford Motor Company had 773 illegal strikes (strikes in violation of the contract or in violation of federal law). The benefits did make the union strong in membership and sound in finances, but this very strength made high union offices attractive to ambitious members, who were not always the best leaders, and inter-union political strife emerged.

Like all people whether rich or poor, Henry was not spared deep grief. Edsel died May 26, 1943. He was forty-nine years old. Sixteen months before he had been operated on for a stomach malady and never fully recovered.

Much of Edsel's time had been taken up with the administration of Willow Run. He had headed a group of Ford executives which went to San Diego, California, in January 1941 at the request of the government to view the Consolidated Aircraft Corporation plant and decide whether or not Ford could build four-engined bombers on a mass production basis.

All Detroit mourned Edsel. He had been a prominent figure in its life. He had been a member of the Arts Commission of the Detroit Institute of Arts since 1925 and was elected president of the Institute in 1930. With his wife, Eleanor, he was a generous donor and his contributions enriched many departments of the museum.

Edsel had found his relaxation with his family and at games of golf and tennis. For many years he had been a frequent spectator at tennis matches and was a follower of the Detroit Tigers baseball team.

Edsel had a great deal to do with the design of all Ford cars following the Model T. The Lincoln cars were largely designed and manufactured under his direction. He had seen changes of great magnitude occur in the automotive business. He had tried to cope with the problems of the laboring man. The workers would miss him, too.

Henry took over the presidency of the company again. For a man of eighty years, his schedule was a strenuous one. It would have tired a man half that age. He was up at five-thirty in the morning. He took a vigorous walk around his estate and had breakfast. Then he would be on his way to Willow Run where the Liberator bombers

were moving along assembly lines. He would attend con-
ferences and approve or reject any changes to be made.
He would walk miles through the shops inspecting work
in all departments. After that he would visit the power
plant at the Rouge, and go on to other parts of the plant
the rest of the day. He had never had the habit of sitting
in his private office for more than a few minutes at a time.
His whole life had been an example of hard work, in-
domitable courage, and clean living.

At the end of the war Henry was greatly relieved when
the huge war contracts were canceled and his factories
could go back on peacetime work. His vast war production had only been waste to him. It had been used
only for destruction.

With the company again making cars, trucks and tractors, Henry made a big decision. He knew he would not
live too many more years and he wanted to see Ford
Motor Company under its new leadership while he was
still living. He made his oldest grandson, Henry II, who
was now twenty-eight years old, the new president.

When Henry handed over the reins to Young Henry,
he realized every generation has its own problems to
solve in industry. He knew Young Henry would have to
form new policies and find answers to increasing difficulties in labor relations that were troubling the
country.

CHAPTER 30

HENRY WATCHED YOUNG HENRY step into his shoes with great interest. He had every confidence in his grandson's ability even if he had not cared about building engines when he was a boy. He had managed the varsity crew while he attended Yale and liked a good race as well as his grandfather. In the race with Chevrolet, Henry hoped the boy would give them a run for their money. He wanted Ford to be first in automobile manufacture more than anything else in the world.

In 1926 Ford had been selling 41 percent of the cars produced in America. By 1941 the percentage had dwindled to only 16 percent. Henry watched Young Henry bring the percentage back to 22 percent in 1946. He was very pleased. "That boy'll do all right," he told Clara, proudly.

"But our grandson isn't doing things the way you did," Clara challenged, her eyes twinkling.

"Shucks," said Henry, "this is a new industrial era, Clara. He's got a couple of my ideas, though, that he can't go wrong with. He wants to build better cars and trucks and tractors at a lower cost than competitors in order to make them available at lower prices to more and more people. He's sold on the idea of serving the public, too. And you just wait until the public sees the new model he's going to bring out. I hope I'll still be around."

But Henry didn't live to see the new model the Ford engineers were working on.

In June 1946, the year after the end of the war, Detroit prepared for one of the most auspicious occasions in all its history, the Golden Jubilee of the automobile industry — fifty years of auto making.

A ten-day celebration paid tribute to the pioneers whose work half a century before founded the new form of transportation. The new transportation had changed the American way of life and swept over the world.

The celebration included dedicating a towering monument, a pageant, a parade, a jubilee revue, an antique exposition contrasting ancient models with the new, a community street jamboree, and a dinner in honor of twelve old-timers.

Detroit gilded the main street. They fired bombs. They closed shops, factories, and stores, and nearly a million people watched a four-hour parade, a panorama of the evolution of the motorcar. There were cars of all shapes and descriptions throughout their history, with drivers and riders dressed to fit the style of the car. Some of the early models broke down and had to be pushed.

Henry had a prominent place at the dinner in honor of the auto pioneers. He liked being called the father of the auto assembly line. Seated close to Henry were R. E. Olds, of Reo and Oldsmobile fame, Barney Oldfield, noted racing driver, Charles E. Nash of the Nash-Kelvinator Corporation, J. Frank Duryea, who helped his late brother Charles build the first gasoline-powered auto in 1893, and Edgar L. Apperson, an early designer of axles and brakes. These old-timers had all lived to see the automobile business become one of the greatest industries in the world.

The first week in April 1947 Clara and Henry came home from a visit in Georgia to find the River Rouge in a violent state. A spring flood had sent the river madly out of its banks. The swirling waters defied the high fences and guards Henry had built around his estate. Tall electric-light poles toppled and cables were waterlogged and short-circuited. Servants in Henry's stone mansion piled logs into the big fireplaces for heat. They used kerosene lamps and candles for a glimmer of light. Nature was exhibiting her gargantuan strength.

The morning of the seventh, Henry had his chauffeur drive him to the Rouge plant to inspect the flood damage.

The challenge of controlling this mad power of the River Rouge brought fire to the shrewd, misty eyes of the old man. Although he was eighty-three, he felt good and made plans to continue his inspection the next morning.

As usual he went to bed at nine o'clock. He dropped off to sleep. Two hours later he was awake. "Clara," he called, and Clara was instantly by his side, just as she had been for fifty-nine years.

"I feel ill. I have a bad headache," Henry said. "I'd like a drink of water."

Clara gave him a glass of water. The house phones were dead because of the flood, so Clara sent the chauffeur to the Ford engineering laboratories, half a mile away, to telephone the doctor in Detroit.

When the doctor arrived, Henry was dead. He had died quietly, as Clara held his hand.

Always through their long married life Clara was at Henry's side. He never wanted her out of his sight. Throughout the years they had lived gently and as devotedly as a young bride and groom, finding joy and comfort in the presence of each other.

CHAPTER 31

YOUNG HENRY DID not merely walk into the Rouge
plant and pick out a nice shiny mahogany desk.
After he attended Yale, he worked as a grease monkey in
the company garage. He wanted to do the dirtiest work.
He resented being treated differently from any other
worker.

He never had had the great love for engines his grandfather had, but he did like working in the dynamometer
rooms and experimental shops. The chief engineer reported that he was always asking questions and had a
terrific appetite for knowledge.

In the spring of 1941 Young Henry enlisted in the
Navy. He was given an ensign's commission and sent to
The Great Lakes Naval Training Station. He wanted to
go to sea, but his father died and he was put on inactive
duty and came to the Rouge plant. The Navy discipline

was valuable to him because he learned to do what he was told to do when he was told to do it.

People didn't think too much about Young Henry's becoming the president of Ford Motor Company as long as his grandfather was still around to steer the ship. But just as soon as Henry died, the world was bulging with curiosity as to just how Young Henry would run the huge industry.

Young Henry plunged into his executive tasks with the great zest of a leader. A few years before he was a quiet, pleasant, blue-eyed, apple-cheeked boy with a disposition to put off crossing bridges until he got to them. He still wore his crew haircut and boyish smile. He was a large man — more than six feet tall and about two hundred pounds in weight. He liked frankness and had no use for high-sounding phrases and big words.

Newspapers and national magazines sent writers to find out about plans for the Ford Motor Company. The American people had always been interested in Henry Ford and his universal car — what was going to happen to that universal car?

There were great problems for Young Henry, problems of industrial development, post-war reorganization, and personnel relations, vastly different from the ones his grandfather had after World War I. Young Henry thought about these things all day in his office and at night when he went home to his wife, Anne, and their two daughters, Charlotte and Baby Anne.

The company, Young Henry realized, had been his grandfather's one-man show. He knew he was not an industrial genius like his grandfather, nor did he believe an industry should be a one-man show. Young Henry thought that a lot of good heads could find better answers to the many great problems. He wanted a team which would pull together to solve problems and plan for the future of the company.

So he started his big team by selecting ten men from inside the company and from outside who were best qualified to give him advice. This management group he called the policy committee. These men were experts in manufacturing, engineering, sales and advertising, industrial relations, purchasing, finance, and legal counsel. Benson Ford, Young Henry's brother, had joined the company in 1946. He was also a member of the policy committee. In 1948 Benson was elected vice-president of the company and director of the Lincoln-Mercury division. The Mercury car had been designed and produced in 1938 to give a vehicle in the lower medium price field. It was named by Edsel.

When the writers came to see Young Henry, he was glad to tell them about his goals. He told them that he realized goals were a lot easier to state than achieve.

First, he wanted to outsell Chevrolet in the low-price field. Second, he wanted to get the Ford share of the total market. He wanted to get back to that 45 to 50 percent his grandfather and his father had won and lost years ago.

"Unless we can do these two things and make a profit to renew our plant, invest for the future, and meet competition on equal terms, the Ford Motor Company will not have any future," Young Henry told reporters. "If we do this job right, make more and better cars to sell for lower and lower prices, we will be making the kind of contribution to society a business like this should make."

When reporters asked Young Henry to make sweeping statements and predictions about world affairs, unlike his grandfather, Young Henry did not pretend to be a prophet. He would merely look interested and say, "I wish I knew the answers."

Young Henry's idea about a big team did not stop with the policy committee. He wanted all the 140,000 Ford workers to be team players. This, he thought, could be brought about if each person in the organization treated the men he worked with as he would like to be treated himself. He told his workers that part of each man's job was to try to get along with the people with whom he worked. He wanted men on every level to be good managers and let the men below them know what decisions were being made that would affect them and why. And wherever possible the men should be given a chance to help make these decisions. He believed this would help introduce democracy into industry. "This is important," Young Henry said, "because machines alone do not give us mass production. Mass production is achieved by both machines and men."

An employee may perform only one operation on an assembly line. It is difficult for this individual to feel that he is an important unit — a member of the team.

This is especially true if he receives no information about the company's objectives and the methods by which it hopes to achieve them. He cannot be expected to show much interest in his job or the company.

Young Henry was ready to tackle his big problem. He wrote a letter to every employee of the Ford Motor Company. In this letter he told the employees:

> We have definitely taken one road. We are headed toward building better cars and trucks and tractors at a lower cost than our competitors, so that we can make them available at lower prices to more and more people in this country and throughout the world.
>
> That's our job. That's what we can do as a team for the American people. We are a manufacturing company. Our job is to give them the best products at the lowest costs. Management can't be the boss here and neither can labor. We work for the American people.
>
> If we are going to progress successfully in the direction we have chosen, we must do it through teamwork — better teamwork than our competitors. . . .
>
> We here at Ford are committed to the idea that it is possible to have low costs and high wages. We also know that if we can reduce our costs and prices while raising our wages, it will be only because Ford men and women — individually and as a team — are more skillful and more efficient than the men and women in any other production team in the industry.

The effect of that letter was good. Many of the employees even went to the trouble to write Young Henry, expressing opinions and reflecting attitudes that were very interesting to the people who had charge of improving working conditions and attitudes of the workers. So

Young Henry decided to send each employee a question-naire in an attempt to discover exactly how he felt about his job.

Seventy percent of those replying did not feel that the company personnel policies had been completely or satis-factorily explained to them. Seventy percent felt that little or no effort had been made to make them feel like a member of the Ford team. Seventy percent did not feel that a fair opportunity had been given for them to make suggestions and criticisms about company practices and officials. Forty-four percent did not feel they had an adequate opportunity to talk over their work or ideas with their immediate superiors. Ninety percent felt that such questionnaires were extremely useful, or at least had some value.

It was obvious to Young Henry that the company had a job to do. A handbook was prepared for all employees outlining the health and safety programs, employee bene-fits, company history and company policies and regula-tions. Eighteen newspapers were circulated to reach all employees in order to keep the men and women better informed about company policies, plans and programs.

An employee suggestion system was inaugurated. The recreation program was expanded so that more than 25,000 employees took part each month in more than forty different activities. The no-smoking rule in Ford plants and offices was abolished.

Young Henry set about developing one of the most extensive educational programs in the industry. An average of 6,500 employees participated each week in programs which ranged from apprenticeship and supervisory training classes to advanced management courses. If a worker had the gumption and will to advance, every facility was offered him.

It was not too long before Young Henry could see that all these things were paying dividends. There was a definite decline in labor turnover.

CHAPTER 32

PEOPLE ALL OVER THE WORLD read about Young Henry's team ideas with interest, but what they really wanted to know was: what changes would be made in the universal car. But that information was kept a deep, dark secret!

On June 1, 1948, when the new Ford was ready for market, Young Henry thought the employees should be the first to see the new models. Each man and woman of the Ford Motor Company received a written invitation from Young Henry. It read:

> It is my pleasure to invite you and members of your family to attend the Ford Family Day program at our Engineering Test Track in Dearborn on Sunday, June 13.
>
> This program has been planned so that you and members of your family can see our new 1949

Ford cars before they are shown to the general public. Our new line of Lincolns, Mercurys, trucks, tractors and motor coaches also will be on display.

The Test Track, on Oakwood Boulevard across from the Dearborn Inn, will be open from 9 a.m. until 9 p.m. on June 13. Due to the anticipated crowds, may I suggest you plan to visit the exhibit before 8 p.m. Plenty of free parking space will be available.

Please bring this letter with you for identification because, as you know, the Test Track is closed to the general public.

I hope you will be able to attend.

Yours sincerely,

HENRY FORD II

It was a beautiful bright, sunny day for Young Henry's party. Every precaution was taken for the comfort and pleasure of the visitors. Booths dotted the acres of test area, dispensing thousands of free hot dogs, ice cream cones, and bottles of pop. Picnic tables were set up at frequent intervals and those thoughtful enough to have prepared lunch dined under canopies. At the farther end of the exhibit area a large orchestra played loud and long. A Red Cross tent was in service but had few calls.

Ford workers from every department, accompanied by their families, came in an almost endless procession to see the completed cars in which they had had some part. Porters, high-priced engineers, pretty stenographers, foundry workers, dressed in their Sunday best, oh-ed and ah-ed over the spectacle. All but the assembly line workers saw for the first time the final results of their labors in the form of the shiny new cars.

The new Model B-A, the fourth big model change in

the Ford forty-five-year history, was Young Henry's bid to recapture supremacy from Chevrolet and Plymouth. In one sweeping model change Young Henry had brought the Ford not merely even with Chevrolet and Plymouth but out in front of them, at least until they too could come up with completely new post-war cars.

The B-A was a surprise all right! It had all the latest luxuries and mechanical advances. No one could ever guess it was remotely related to its ancestors, only the 8-cylinder model's V-type engine resembled in some degree the previous V-8.

Young Henry's team had made a thorough study of what the public wanted in an inexpensive automobile. They wanted ROOM. So the B-A gave them sofa-wide seats, with lots of hip and shoulder room, and 57 percent more luggage space. And new "Picture Window" visibility all around.

They wanted SAFETY. So the B-A gave 59 percent more rigid "Life-guard" body and frame structure. The new "Magic Action" king-size brakes used the car's forward motion to help stop the car, making stopping 35 percent easier.

They wanted COMFORT. So the B-A had a "Midship" Ride. By moving the engine five inches forward, the designers were able to place the rear seat ahead of the rear axle, lessening the effect of road shocks on passengers. The engineers dropped the transverse springs typical of the company's suspension system since Henry made the model T in 1908. Rear springs were now the conventional longitudinal type. Front suspension was on coil springs, and all four corners of the chassis had airplane type shock absorbers.

They wanted ECONOMY. So the B-A had a new lubrication system. It was called "Equa-Flo" Cooling and "Deep Breath" Manifolding, which saved up to ten percent on gas. Even greater savings were possible with the new Overdrive, which was optional at extra cost.

They wanted BEAUTY. So the B-A was a sight for Ford eyes. Body and chassis adopted the wide flat style. There were no rear fenders. Overall length and width virtually was the same as the 1948 model, but the height was reduced nearly three and a half inches. The front end had a simple grille design dominated by a massive round medallion. A single, long chrome "rub rail" protected the body and created a long, fleet look.

Mechanically minded people gathered around an exhibit where an engineer hovered over a new Ford chassis, eager to answer questions. Those who knew the V-8 were quick to see the mechanical advantages in the new '49 Ford. The complete new "Equa-Flo" system was a great improvement. All coolant flowed through every part of the system, making uniform temperatures throughout with no hot spots or steam pockets. There were two water pumps — one for each bank of cylinders, forcing coolant through the system at high velocity and with great force for more efficient heat transfer.

The engine exhaust cross-over pipe had been brought

forward. In the old model the pipe ran underneath the motor and the oil-pan could not be removed without removing the pipe.

Many people said that the springs would be the biggest selling point. Customers could no longer say, "The Ford still has those old stiff springs." Instead of the two-spring suspension in the V-8 there was now four-spring suspension — two large coil springs in front and two semi-elliptic leaf type in the rear.

Mechanics were happy to see the oil pipe in front of the motor. In the old models a man needed overalls and practically had to stand on a stepladder to drop oil into the pipe placed in back of the motor. This new arrangement was very handy to service.

All Ford owners were familiar with the "hump" on the floor of the back seat. Lowering the position of the drive shaft into the differential eliminated the "hump." This made a roomier and more comfortable back seat, although it took away the cause of many humorous remarks.

Another exhibit demonstrated the operation of the car. Each step could be carefully watched. The operator explained that as he stepped on the starter the car was in neutral gear, ignition turned on, clutch disengaged; then as the motor started the piston started to travel on the suction stroke. This brought gasoline mixture into the the motor as it started the compression stroke. When the piston got to the top of the cylinder, the distributor was ready to deliver fire to the spark plug at the time the piston reached the top of its travel. After the explosion the piston started downward on the power stroke. As the piston came back up, the burned gas was released through the exhaust valve.

"The automobile engine," the operator explained, "like the stationary gas engine, has a flywheel which rotates whenever the engine is operating. The clutch, in back of the flywheel, disconnects the engine and the rear wheels, allowing the engine to run while the car is stationary." The engine was now going at high speed but the wheels were not moving. "It is the job of the gears to transmit the force from the engine to the rear wheels," the operator said. Transmission gears (back of the clutch) and differential gears (in the middle of the rear axle) transmit this force. The differential also permits one rear wheel to go faster than the other, which is necessary, when a car is going around a corner.

With the clutch disengaged, the operator moved the shifting lever to low gear. The car moved slowly. The operator again disengaged the clutch and moved the shifting lever to second gear. After enough speed was gained, the shifting lever was moved to high gear. The man in charge of this demonstration drove slowly around a small track. He was then ready to explain the same operations to a new group of observers.

Visitors were not as much interested in what the new developments were called as what they did. They were interested in the fact that engineering and research were giving them a car that was easier to stop and safer to drive. This new car was more comfortable, convenient, and had smoother performance; it also had better pick-up, and was a gasoline saver.

The B-A was new from the ground up. It set new standards of beauty, comfort, performance, and safety in the low-priced automobile field. Even the fussiest customer would be able to find a style and color to appeal to him. Luscious colors such as sea-mist green, birch gray, colony blue, gun-metal gray, fez red, and Miami cream covered the new creations and completed the "new look."

To accomplish all this in a short time, the new team more than tripled the men in the Engineering Division. Not only did they need 2600 men to work out a complete new line of cars, but to work on improvements that the public would not see for three to five years.

The slogan "There's a new Ford in your future" blazed its way across America in comic strips, movie skits, radio programs, magazines, newspapers, billboards, and across the sky on a blimp.

The whole world was watching the race for leadership in the light-car field. But the real test could not come until cars became plentiful enough for a buyer to have a choice instead of being lucky to get any kind. One thing was evident, Young Henry was up on his toes and expected to give the customers what they wanted — not what one man thought was good for them.

By this time Young Henry was convinced there was no secret formula for insuring that management and labor get along peacefully together. He was sure, however, if

some degree of peace were to be attained the principles of conduct that must be followed by each party were:

1. A conscientious and honest desire and ability to understand the other's viewpoint.

2. A willingness to lay all except the secret and confidential facts face up on the table for the other party to examine.

3. Unlimited patience in mutual dealings, whether it be those across the important negotiation table or those that exist from day to day operations.

It would take years for Young Henry to achieve the goals he had set for himself, but he had made an excellent start. If he could prove to his workers that they were no longer numbers, but individuals whose work was recognized, and that their own company could actually do more for them than unions, then a great business would not be too big to be human. Men would not be compelled to strike for proper conditions and just rewards. Then industry would have what it has needed ever since Young Henry's grandfather introduced mass production.

On Young Henry's desk was a picture of his grandfather, the great man who put America on wheels. In a shed an industry was born and grew and grew and was still growing. Young Henry often thought about his grandfather's many achievements and convictions. Building a sound business of service that would last and last was a principle theory to be well remembered. With new methods in a new era Young Henry was ready to make his contribution to America.

THE END